Mary Llewellyn,
The Corner House,
Virginia Water,
Surrey
→

E.M.F.

Prelude

The child jumped back

(See page 11)

C. H. ABRAHALL

PRELUDE

Illustrated by
ANNA ZINKEISEN

OXFORD UNIVERSITY PRESS
Geoffrey Cumberlege
1947

OXFORD UNIVERSITY
PRESS
AMEN HOUSE, WARWICK SQUARE
LONDON, E.C.4.
Edinburgh Glasgow New York
Toronto Melbourne Cape Town
Bombay   Calcutta   Madras

GEOFFREY CUMBERLEGE
PUBLISHER TO THE
UNIVERSITY

PRINTED 1947 IN GREAT BRITAIN BY RICHARD CLAY AND COMPANY LTD.
BUNGAY, SUFFOLK.
579

CONTENTS

Foreword

OFTEN I have wondered what a child must feel like who is born with some great gift and the spark which urges expression.

Thanks to Eileen Joyce, I have had the privilege of probing back into her childhood days, and all the reactions which went with them. At times, it has been a little difficult for her to remember or re-capture the past. On these occasions I have used an author's licence, and drawn upon my own imagination, even to conjuring up a few fictitious characters with which to surround her. It is only when we are growing old that our childhood returns crystal clear, and my heroine is still young and at the height of her career.

It is my hope that this story which Miss Joyce has generously let me use, will prove an inspiration to many youthful musicians and young people interested in the arts.

C. H. A.

CHAPTER I

The Hermit

"TWINK! Twi—nk! Come back!" The exasperated voice of a small girl who was running in hot pursuit of a little kangaroo along a mountain path in Tasmania caused an echo to come floating back, but not the kangaroo. Instead, he increased his long, ambling hops and disappeared round a bend.

"Oh, Twink, you are a nuisance." She stopped for a moment to catch her breath and realized, looking around for the first time, that she had come much higher up the mountain path than she had intended. The great fertile plain below had never seemed so small and far away, and the towering, precipitous mountains all around her seemed so close that she knew she had disobeyed her mother's orders and climbed too far. But the air was crisp and invigorating, she was not in the least afraid of the mountain and she wanted her kangaroo. So with a last glance behind her at the smoke ascending from a tiny shack below, she turned and once again began to climb the path.

"Twink, where are you going?" Again the childish voice rang out, this time a little breathlessly, for she was manœuvring a particularly difficult piece of path that passed between two great boulders and needed very careful climbing. Squeezing through, she stopped in surprise, for in front of her, on a jutting crag, looking almost as if it were constructed on air, stood a crude hut made of logs. For a moment she drew back and gazed at it gravely. Was it a rest house or the haunt of some lonely hermit? The door was open, but there was an unearthly stillness all around. Then something laughed, horribly— a loud, discordant, yelling cry. The child jumped back against the boulder, for the moment connecting the cry with the hut. The next minute, however, she relaxed, and a smile flitted across her face as a laughing jackass glided into the open and perched on a crag. At first the great bird seemed to be surveying her solemnly with its large grave eyes, but the next moment it raised its crest in anger. The child, realizing that the jackass was not looking at her, but at a ridge just above her head, glanced up and shrank back in sudden fear, for the one thing that could strike terror to her small soul was upon her in the shape of a small, evil-looking snake. Venom was in its wicked beady eyes as it slithered softly towards her. Paralysed with fright, she watched; then once again came that terrible yelling, mocking laugh followed by a whirr of wings and a dart of colour as the jackass swooped down upon its prey. He struck with his powerful beak, caught up the reptile and was away. With a little gasp, the child slithered to the ground just as a man's voice broke the silence.

"Here, what's all this?" Strong hands picked her up and carried her into the hut. With great gentleness the man laid her on a rough bed, chafed her hands and moistened her lips with water.

"Ah, that's better." He sat back and allowed himself to be stared at by a pair of big, wondering eyes which reminded him of the waters of Tasmania, deep, yet alive with reflections. This long-legged shoeless child with her vivid chestnut hair, and tattered clothes, was an odd enough sight herself, he thought.

"What's your name?" he asked gently.

"Eileen."

"That's a pretty name. Any more?"

"Joyce. What's yours?"

"You may call me Daniel."

"Are you a hermit?"

Daniel saw a troubled look flit across the face of the speaker.

"Some people like to call me that," Daniel said

and laughed. The laugh made them friends at once. Eileen joined in and she became alive, sparkling and vivacious. It changed her from a rather solemn little girl to one brimming over with fun.

" I thought hermits were old. My mother says they don't like children. I expect that's just to stop me climbing the mountains."

" I expect it is," Daniel said drily. " Where do you come from ? " he added.

" Down on the plain."

" You've climbed a long way. Do you think it's wise to wander so far alone ? "

" Twink ran away."

" And who may Twink be ? "

" A kangaroo. My Daddy found him when he was a baby. He is quite tame, but he *will* run away."

" He'll have to be spoken to," Daniel said seriously, and as he stood up Eileen shot a quick, searching glance in his direction. He was big and strong, his hair iron grey, his face lined and weather-beaten. His eyes were the bluest and kindest she had ever seen.

" Why aren't you looking for gold ? " she asked. " Everyone who lives here goes away to look for gold. My Daddy has."

" I did once," said Daniel, doing something with a kettle. " That's why I came to live here, right away from it. I prefer this." He took a small object out of his pocket and ran it caressingly along his lips, rendering a few soft notes.

" What's that ? " Eileen sprang towards him, an excited quiver in her voice.

" Music ; listen." He broke into a quick lilting refrain. The small harmonica seemed to dance under his hand, and as he played the tense, rapt expression on Eileen's face changed and began instead to reflect the lights and shades of the tune.

" Again, again ! " She clapped her hands excitedly as Daniel stopped, half amused by the strange, unaccountable excitement he had aroused in his small audience.

" A tune you should know," he said, and broke into the refrain of " John Peel," written and composed in Tasmania itself.

" Let me try—please let me try ! " There was such urgency in Eileen's voice that he stopped playing and stared at her in surprise, then, getting up, went over to a huge chest and began searching for something.

" Does music give you a funny feeling ? " he asked from the depths.

" How funny ? " Eileen came and stood beside him, impatiently wondering if he was going to let her try to play.

" Well, I don't exactly know. Make you want to make it ? " Having found what he was looking for, he sat back on his heels and handed something to her. " See what you make of that." He got the answer to his question, for with hands that trembled and with a quick, fleeting smile of joy, Eileen took from him a duplicate of his own instrument. For a moment she gazed at it as if fascinated, then very softly blew.

"Here, like this; try to copy me." Daniel played a few notes, and was surprised at the quickness with which she caught them.

"Now this." Almost as excited as his pupil, he went on a little more. With a few faults she followed him, then paused, a tragic look on her face.

"It was wrong," she said.

"Doesn't matter, you'll soon learn. Try this."

"No, it was wrong." Eileen stamped her foot with impatience. "Let me get it right."

"You are a funny kid. What's a few mistakes when you are learning? But have it your own way." He went over the few notes again and this time his pupil got them right. He was rewarded once again by that quick smile.

"Come on, let's try another bit." But at that moment a small head came round the door and a penitent kangaroo stared at his mistress.

"Oh, Twink! You are bad." Eileen flung her arms round the kangaroo's neck. It stood up on its hind legs as she did so, and proved to be quite as tall as she was.

"Looks as if you should be off," Daniel warned, "it will soon be dark."

"Oh!" For a moment Eileen regarded him bleakly. She wanted desperately to ask if she could keep the mouth-organ.

" You can take that thing with you—that is, if you will look after it."

" For my own ? "

" Yes, for your own, and if your Ma will let you come up again I will teach you some more."

" I shall come." Eileen reckoned that no parent in the world would be able to stop her now that she had found this new friend. A friend who could show her how to make music.

" I'd better come some of the way with you and next time, young lady, keep your eye open for snakes. There may not always be a helpful jackass about."

" I hate snakes."

" I don't imagine anyone loves them." Daniel walked along with big easy strides, strides that Eileen found hard to keep up with.

" Come on, let's give you a pick-a-back." He paused and bent down.

" What's that ? " asked Eileen.

" Like this," and he heaved her up on to his back. " Gracious me, doesn't your Dad ever play with you this way ? "

" He has to find gold."

" No man ever *has* to find gold, but perhaps I shouldn't say that." There was bitterness in Daniel's voice.

" You may," allowed Eileen from her lofty perch. " Mummie and I never see him now, and we won't any more, until he sends for us to go to Australia."

" Ugh," grunted Daniel. " So that's the idea, is

it ? Well, young lady, I think you can run home from here. Come again soon.''

As if loth to step down from his heights, he put her down on the last reef and stood watching as she ran off, a strange little girl with a still stranger pet.

"Is that you, Eileen?" her mother's voice enquired, as she paused at the door of the shack which was their home. "Where have you been? Your cousin is ill and I have been waiting for you so long to fetch the doctor." Mrs. Joyce sounded weary. It was a hard, unyielding life for a woman all alone, with two young children to care for and little enough money to buy the necessities of life.

"But the doctor is at Zeehen, Mother. How could I get there to-night?"

"You could have borrowed Old Jack's pony, but it is too late now. We shall have to wait till morning. That is, unless I walk it and you stay with John."

"What is the matter with him?" Curiously Eileen tiptoed towards the crude bed on which John tossed uneasily.

"He has some kind of fever."

"It was the apples he ate."

"No, it's not that. How many did he eat?"

"Eight, and they were all green. I betted him he couldn't eat them all. He didn't, he gave me one. He ate the rest."

"Really, Eileen, you children are so stupid. If that is all it is, I will give him some castor oil and wait until morning."

" I'll hold his nose."

" You come near me ! " John opened his eyes and shot his cousin a threatening look. " Sneak," he muttered and turned his face to the wall.

" Mummie has got to get you well," Eileen reasoned, offended at John's remark.

" Don't argue with him, it'll make him worse. Come on, my lad, sit up and take this."

The castor oil administered, Mrs. Joyce went back to her chair, meaning to keep watch over the sick boy, but the toil of too many hard days, water to be carried, logs to be cut, food to be trapped—for they were far from the nearest shop ; clothes to be made ; and a hundred and one other jobs proved too much for her. In a few minutes she was asleep and it was Eileen who remained awake. For the bush of Tasmania taught all those who lived in it, young and old, to be self-reliant. It was a land chiefly composed of very young and very old, for from across the mainland came ever the call of gold. Mr. Joyce had heard that call and had been gone over a year, and thus it was that Eileen and her mother found there was much to turn their hand to.

B

CHAPTER II

A Quick Ear

IT was some weeks before Eileen could escape again to her new-found friend. John had woken up covered with a thick pink rash and feeling very sorry for himself.

" You'll have to help," Mrs. Joyce warned her small daughter. " No wandering off and forgetting to come back. Unless I'm very much mistaken, it's measles."

" Yes, Mum." Eileen walked out on to a kind of broken-down veranda, its roof letting in the daylight and propped up at each end by two tottering poles. She looked wistfully towards the blue mountains and fingered the harmonica clutched in her hand. " I shan't be a minute," she called, and sped away down a pathway towards the river. There was a strange padding sound and Twink was beside her. He tapped her playfully with his already powerful paw, just to show that he wanted to play.

" Not now, Twink, come on," and she ran fleet-footed through thickly growing undergrowth, along a small beaten track to a huge willow tree. Its branches hung heavily down to the ground, and, parting them, she entered her own special sanctum.

The heavy branches shut her off from the outside world, their thickness almost making a tent. Eileen had discovered it one day when she was looking for wood, and her quick imagination had turned it into a fairy palace and furnished it with beautiful things such as her heart craved for. A small tin in which were roses she had gathered a few days before, was, in her eyes, a beautiful blue glass vase, such as she had caught sight of once in an old magazine.

A little moss hummock was her chair, a chair with a high back, with tapestry rich in colour and beautifully blended. A small box was her table, and Twink had his seat made from an old branch of a tree. It was upon this he solemnly sat now, his small head slightly on one side, his little eyes watching his mistress to see if she was getting some particular titbit for him from out of her " safe ". For it was to this " safe " that Eileen was giving her attention. Made from an old biscuit tin and buried up to its lid in the earth, it was here that Eileen kept her particular treasures.

An old rag doll, made by her mother

from a piece of cloth, now faded and worn from much loving. A piece of string, threaded with nuts crudely painted by her father to resemble beads. A saucer, broken in half, but kept specially for imaginary parties. A bottle that went by the name of tea-pot, and her only book, made of rag, its pictures worn away with fingering. Taking out the rag doll, Eileen held her up and surveyed her seriously.

" Esmeralda, you've got to look after my greatest treasure." She began to wrap the harmonica in Esmeralda's skirts, and at that moment a robin sang its plaintive little ditty. For a moment Eileen paused, then very softly she picked out the notes on the harmonica. Again the robin sang and again Eileen answered. That strange, excited look came into her eyes as over and over again she played the notes until they were quite perfect. The robin, anxious to see its challenger, fluttered down on to a twig and watched her, its small head inquisitively on one side.

" Thank you, Robin." Eileen made him a mock curtsey, then reluctantly put the instrument away, safe in the skirts of Esmeralda. She went back to the shack ; but during the next few days, whenever she could steal a moment from looking after John and helping her mother, she stole away to her sanctum to practise and copy the songs of the robin, the finch and the mountain thrush. The sounds of nature all around her were the only music she knew, but her ear was quick and her touch was sure, and she soon

The robin fluttered down on to a twig.

(*See page* 20)

learnt to copy them perfectly. Her excitement as she succeeded gave her an odd feeling of triumph. Her mother found her unusually silent, and fearing she had been too exacting in her demands, she decided to reward Eileen.

" Eileen, I am going to make you a new frock," she said one day.

" But we haven't got any stuff."

" Oh, yes, we have. I've been keeping it until you needed it. Look ! " Mrs. Joyce had been searching in an old tin box as she spoke, and now drew out a richly coloured shawl.

" But you can't cut that up ! " There was horror in Eileen's voice. It was the only really beautiful thing they possessed, a relic of the days when her mother had been young and attractive, a reminder of better times.

" See here, Eileen, I shan't want it again and it's time you had one nice thing, so cut up it's got to be."

Without more ado, Mrs. Joyce took the scissors and began to cut briskly, but the cutting became slower and slower, and with dismay Eileen saw her mother dash some tears angrily from her eyes. Without a word, she turned and ran to her sanctum. It was some hours later that she returned to find the dress completed, and the warm hug she gave her mother conveyed her appreciation of the sacrifice she had made.

" Who would have believed it ? " Mrs. Joyce

stood back to survey her handiwork as Eileen pirouetted before her.

" Believe what ? " Eileen eyed her shyly, feeling suddenly self-conscious in her new finery.

" You are going to have the looks I once had. 'Tis strange, but against that frock your hands make me think of butterflies. I've never noticed them before."

" What's the matter with them ? " Eileen eyed them suspiciously.

" Nothing is the matter with them," laughed her mother. " Now be off to bed, and to-morrow you must get out a little."

" What about me ? " John shouted, for he was feeling better.

" You go to sleep," Mrs. Joyce said, and she turned to her mending and worked steadily until it was too dark to see. Then, as she went to her bed, she paused by Eileen's, and rais-ing her candle, looked at her with a slightly puzzled expression. There was a sensitiveness about this daughter of hers that she failed to understand—a sensitiveness which she feared would go hard with her in the life of the bush, where the whole of life was one grim struggle for existence. She would have liked to have her educated, but it was quite out of the question. With a heavy sigh, she turned away and lay thinking long into the night. Morning, however, found her on her feet again, and soon she was bustling about, preparing a meal for the children and driving Eileen out of the house to do as she pleased.

Eileen was in high spirits. She at once made for her mountain path and went in search of Daniel.

Eagerly she ran up the path and met him coming round the corner, a gun over his shoulder, a knapsack on his back.

'' I thought you had forgotten me ! '' Daniel said as he took her by the hand and they walked back to the hut together.

'' Oh no,'' Eileen exclaimed eagerly.

'' Then let's have a cup of tea, and while I make it let me hear how you have got on with your harmonica.'' Daniel began to get busy while Eileen, sitting on the step of the hut, amused him with her imitations of bird songs.

Daniel was moved and interested by the care with which she had copied the only music she knew, and when they had finished their tea he sat down beside her to teach her some simple melodies. An hour passed all too quickly for both of them. Eileen was an apt pupil, eager to learn more and more, but a sudden cry from a wild bird brought Daniel to his feet.

"Gosh, I'd almost forgotten." He shaded his eyes and looked up into the sky.

"Forgotten what?" Eileen looked at him anxiously.

"My golden eagle. I've lost him."

"Have you got a tame one?"

"Yes. He provides my larder. I had him out of a nest and brought him up myself. He has never gone far and always returns to his perch. But for two days he hasn't come back. I've searched for miles round. Something must have happened to him."

"Let's go and look for him."

"It's no good, Eileen. I expect someone has shot him. I've listened and listened for his bell, but not a sound."

"What bell?" Eileen sounded interested.

"I fixed a little bell round his leg so that I could follow him in his flight."

"Let's go and listen again." All eagerness, Eileen dragged her friend up the path and, without much hope, he followed her. Picking a small pink flower, Eileen tucked it into her hair, dancing on before him, pausing here and there to dabble her feet in a waterfall as it trickled down the mountain, or gather some flowers, venturing upon a more perilous crag to do so.

"Look, Daniel! The world's at our feet." She stood on an overhanging crag, silhouetted against the sky, perfectly fearless and quite unmoved by the great height.

"I thought we had come up to look for Craig," Daniel reminded her.

"Craig? Is that his name?"

"Yes, it sounded big and grand to me. Like him."

"You love him, don't you?" She shot him one of her quick looks.

"Like you love Twink."

"Yes, I know. Then we must find him. Listen to that fall." She paused as the roar of water reached them, growing louder and louder as they went on. "It's lovely!" Eileen cried, as the fall came into view, white and foaming, dancing and chasing, gathering volume as it fell into a large ravine.

"You should see it in a storm," Daniel said. "It's angry then and roars instead of laughs. Come on, we must go back." He turned to retrace his steps, but Eileen seized his hand.

"Listen!" she begged, and stood, her head slightly on one side, a strange alert look in her eyes.

"Ssh!" Eileen went forward a few steps, then paused. She reminded Daniel of a pointer.

"What is it? You can't hear anything above this din!"

"Yes, I can. There it is again. I know it is a bell."

"Where? Dash this row. I can't hear anything."

" It's over here ! " Eileen left the path and climbed into a thick wood of firs and, following her, Daniel also heard the faint tinkle of a bell.

" Well, I'll be jiggered. What sharp ears you have, child," he exclaimed. With quick, easy strides he went through some undergrowth and, parting the thicket, saw before him his missing eagle.

" Craig ! " In a moment he was on his knees beside the great bird, for the proud eagle was grounded. One wing hung limply and was dark with a deep red stain.

" Is he hurt ? " Eileen asked as she came near.

" Keep a little distance away. He is not used to strangers. Yes, someone shot him as he came over the valley, I expect."

" Can you mend his wing ? "

" If I can get him home." Daniel held out his wrist and said encouragingly, " Come, Craig, up old fellow." The eagle closed his eyes as if in great pain, then suddenly opened them and put one huge claw over Daniel's wrist.

" That's better, now the other. Come, Craig, try." He moved his arm slightly, and with a great effort the eagle laboriously hopped on to his arm. Steadying the great bird with his other arm, Daniel rose slowly to his feet.

" That's better. Lead the way, Eileen." Slowly they moved down the mountain side, and not until Daniel had Craig safely on a strong table did he speak again.

"I've got you to thank for this," he smiled.

"Can you mend him now?" Eileen asked.

"If you'll hold the bowl and help me."

"Yes, I will. I often help my mother when the animals are sick."

"Then help me by doing as you are told. I have to remove the bullet." Quickly Daniel slipped a hood over Craig's head, then he worked deftly until the bullet rattled into the tray Eileen was holding. A quick dressing, and in a few moments Craig was tearing happily at the dead carcase of a rabbit which Daniel had thrown him.

"Ugh! I don't like that." Eileen hurried outside.

"You're a funny kid," laughed Daniel. "You don't turn a hair while I dress his wound, yet you rush outside when he has his breakfast."

"It's ugly." Eileen looked at him as if that were quite enough explanation.

"And you don't like ugly things—is that it?"

"Yes, I suppose so. Look, Daniel, there's the moon. Isn't it funny you can see him sometimes in the daytime, but he looks so white. Why does he always look so scornful?" Eileen sat back on her heels and gazed up at the offending personage.

"It's only in this part of the world that he looks so contemptuous," laughed Daniel. "If you were in England you would see quite a different man."

"A different man?" Eileen sounded quite startled.

" Yes, he's a kindly, smiling man there. If you ever go to England, you notice."

" Oh, I shan't ever go there. We haven't any money, and Mummy says a person must have money to travel."

" Not always," Daniel corrected. " Some people work their way round the world."

" But is there really a different man ? "

" Well, I suppose not really. It's just that it is right over the other side of the world and so you see him from a different angle, as it were. Sometimes when I was in England homesick for these mountains, I used to say how-do-you-do to the Tasmanian man."

" How ? " Eileen regarded him with a pair of very serious blue eyes.

" I'll let you into a secret in case you should ever want to do it. There are two ways." Daniel made it all sound very mysterious. " The first is to turn your back on the moon and look between your legs, like this." Daniel suited the action to the words and Eileen went into peals of laughter. He looked so funny, looking at the world upside down.

" Yes, I was afraid you would laugh," Daniel protested, pretending to be offended as he straightened himself ; " the other way is to incline your head to the right."

They wandered a little way from the hut and climbed on to a great crag. Eileen took out her harmonica and began to play the tunes she had just learnt while Daniel, with his hat tilted over his eyes, sat listening. His presence had made a great difference in her life. She did not want to play with Esmeralda any more, and the imaginary people she used to conjure up began to fade. Instead, she held long conversations with her mouth-organ, making it answer her in music.

" If there isn't music born in you I'll eat my hat," Daniel remarked after a while, as she glanced up at him.

" Play to me," she begged eagerly, and as he played, the moon became golden and the mountains and lakes below became startlingly beautiful in the soft light.

" I must take you home." Daniel got up and swung her on to his shoulders and started down the mountain path.

" Why do you carry me ? " she asked.

" Because you can't keep up with me," he teased.

" I can," she answered indignantly.

" If you run, maybe, and then what would your Ma say if you arrived all out of breath as if someone had been chasing you ? "

" She is used to my running. Will you come and see her sometime ? "

" Maybe," said Daniel, and, after he had put her down, he stood and watched his young friend run the rest of the way and vanish into the shack. He walked home thoughtfully, wondering if there was anything he could do to help her future, for he realized that she had a quick brain, and that the music which seemed to be a part of her must somehow be given a chance to develop.

Meanwhile, however, Eileen was facing her first real upheaval. A letter had arrived at last from her father, and Old Joe, the carrier, who had been fetched to read it, had made it quite plain that the time had come for them to leave Tasmania and sail to the mainland of Australia. Mr. Joyce wanted them to go as soon as possible. Kununoppin, a small mining town near Koolgardie, was to be their destination, and he enclosed some money to help them on their way.

"But Twink—and—and Daniel and all the people we know," sobbed Eileen, "will we never see them again?"

"That remains to be seen." Mrs. Joyce tried to comfort her daughter as best she could, but that night Eileen refused to be comforted.

CHAPTER III

The Piano

THE week that followed was a difficult one for Eileen. Old Joe, the carrier, turned up with a couple of large packing-cases, and after their arrival the only home she had ever known was stripped of all familiar things and was home no longer.

" It'll be fun," announced John, who was filled with the adventure of the whole thing. " We shall go in a train, and—and in a ship, and it'll be a bigger country than this, and Mum says there'll be a school and other boys to play with. Not that I want to go to school," he added hastily.

" They'll make you," Eileen warned.

" They'll have to catch me first," laughed her cousin and ran out of the door and away down to the river to see if he had caught any crawfish in his home-made pots.

" We shall have to leave a good deal behind," said Mrs. Joyce, bustling in, her arms full of belongings. " We shall have to have a sale."

" What about Twink ? " Eileen managed at last to voice the dread that was spoiling any enjoyment that she might have felt.

" Twink ? " Her mother paused and dumped the things on a box.

" Yes, Twink—I won't leave him behind." The words were out, and now Eileen stood facing her mother, her face white, a defiant look in her eyes.

"But, Eileen, you can't take him. It's going to be difficult to make the journey ourselves. We shall have to trek some of the way once we have landed. Your father has not sent enough money for the whole journey by train. I know how you love Twink, but it just cannot be managed."

"Then I won't go—I won't go!" Eileen stamped her foot in anger, then with horror she realized that tears were not far away. To make it worse, Twink at that moment entered and came rushing up to his young mistress.

"He is getting big, child. I know it would be madness. Far better to leave him behind than perhaps get him some of the way and then have to part with him." Seeing her daughter's distress, Mrs. Joyce tried to be patient and explain, but Eileen was in no mood for reason. Her mind was filled with all sorts of wild ideas. She would run away and take Twink with her. She would not leave Tasmania without him. If her mother could not find her, they could not go. Somehow she must make her mother understand that she meant what she said.

c

" Come, Twink ! " She turned suddenly and made
for the door.

" Eileen, where are you going ? I want you here ! "
But Mrs. Joyce's words fell on deaf ears, for Eileen
was running like a wild thing towards the mountains
with Twink outstripping her. She ran until she was
almost exhausted and her legs began to feel like cotton
wool. Then, suddenly, she flung herself down and
gave way to a passion of tears, for the threatened parting with Twink was the first real grief she had ever
felt. Twink, distressed by this strange sound from
his mistress, came and nuzzled her in a puzzled
fashion. " Oh, Twink, you would be better dead ! "
she sobbed, flinging her arms round him.

Daniel came upon this tragic little tableau as he
walked down the path. " Here, here, young lady, we
can't have this. Real tears ? What's it all about ? "

" Oh, Daniel, it's—it's so awful ! "

Daniel found himself clutched round the neck, and
as he knelt down beside Eileen, a very wet face was
pressed against his.

" Come, now, Eileen, it can't be as bad as all this.
There's always a bright side." He held her close and
rose to his feet. " Let's go up to the hut and you can
tell me all about it."

Loud sniffs rewarded him, and he knew that the
storm was abating.

" Craig is better, you will be pleased to know."

" Can he fly yet ? " Eileen raised her head suddenly
and looked at him.

" Not yet, his wing is not quite mended."

" I think I'll walk now."

" There you are, then." Daniel put her down and for a moment they walked along in silence.

" Where are you going ? " Eileen asked.

" To call on you."

" On me ? "

" Yes, you haven't been to see me for some days. I thought you might be ill."

" Oh ! "

" Let's sit here." Daniel indicated an inviting spot and lay down. Eileen squatted beside him. Tilting his hat over his eyes, Daniel was fully aware that he was being studied. It seemed as if Eileen were trying to make up her mind to say something, and he guessed that she found it difficult.

" I think you had better tell me," he said at last.

" I've—I've run away ! "

" Why ? "   Daniel showed no surprise.

" Because we are leaving Tasmania, and Mummie—won't let me take Twink."

" So that's it ! "   Daniel sat up and regarded Eileen for a moment.

" And," said Eileen seriously, " there's you, too."

" First partings are always the worst ones, but it's Twink we've got to think about."

" Daniel, I can't leave him behind."

" What about leaving him with me ? "

" With you ? "

" Yes, why not ?   He knows me and, I think, likes me.   When you get to Australia, if you find it's the sort of place where you think he would be happy, you can write to me and I'll get someone to bring him along."

" Oh, Daniel, would you ? "

" Yes, of course.   But promise me this.   If you are in a town and think he'll be unhappy, you've got to be honest and think of him first, and let him stay with me."

" Yes, yes, I will ; and it won't really be good-bye, will it ?   And he does like you."   Eileen's eyes were shining again now that the certainty of never seeing Twink again was removed.   " And what about us ? " she asked.

" One day I shall come to hear you play."

" Play ?   Play what ? "

" I dunno, but you will play something.   A piano,

violin—who knows ?—but it'll be something, and don't forget I told you so."

" Daniel, you *are* funny. Got anything to eat ? "

" Yes, in the hut. I'll race you ! " Happiness restored, they ran to the hut, and made a hearty meal from scones Daniel had made, a tin of peaches and some rich plum cake. Daniel told her stories of Australia, and for the first time she began to feel excited.

" To-morrow I'll come down and give your mother a hand with the packing-cases ; and remember you've got to write and tell me everything that happens."

" But, Daniel "—there was sudden horror in Eileen's voice—" I can't write."

" You soon will. They'll teach you when you get over there."

" And will you write to me and tell me all about Twink ? "

" You bet I will."

After Eileen had left him Daniel sat thoughtfully for a time, and then jumped up suddenly and began putting a few of his possessions into a kit-bag, after which he searched around for a bit of leather, and in a few moments was busy making a collar to fit a small kangaroo. He worked late into the night, studded it with brass until it was a collar fit to thrill the heart of any child when worn by her own particular pet. At last, tired out, he flung himself down and slept.

Eileen awoke early the next morning—her last day in Tasmania—and, dressing hurriedly, ran out of the

shack and along the road towards Zeehen, the small
village near her home. It was a glorious morning and
Twink ran beside her, grabbing his breakfast from
young shoots as they ran. Eileen paused long enough
to wash her face in a cool, clear stream, then singing
lustily, ran on towards the village. The day was to
be a good one. Derek and Mavis, two friends of hers
from Zeehen, had sent word to say that they would
be over to say good-bye, and some of the neighbours
had promised to come over to tea. Old Joe was to
fetch them, and the Joyces were to have a good
send-off.

" Look, Twink, there they are ! " Eileen exclaimed
excitedly as she saw, far along the road, two children
on ponies galloping towards them.

" Let's sit and wait for them." Twink, extremely
interested, followed Eileen to a boulder and sat down
close beside her. He put his soft nose against her
neck and she felt an uncomfortable, warning lump in
her throat as she realized that it was their last day
together. Getting up abruptly, she jumped down,
and this time did not stop running until Derek's
cheery voice greeted her.

" Hullo, Eileen, aren't we nice and early ? Come
on, jump up behind." He reined in and Eileen was
soon seated, her arms round his waist. " Come on,
Mavis, let's race ! " His pony was bigger than his
sister's and carried the two of them well. Twink was
hard put to it to keep up with the two ponies as, with
laughter and shouts, the party raced towards the shack.

"Good morning, children," Mrs. Joyce greeted them. "Our tea-party is to be at four o'clock, Eileen, so mind you are all there in time."

"We will be, Mrs. Joyce," Derek promised, and having tethered their ponies, they set off to Eileen's sanctum, which, for the remainder of the day, they made their headquarters. In the afternoon they climbed up to see Daniel, but there was no sign of him and the hut looked unnaturally tidy and swept up.

"Now I won't see him." Eileen sounded crest-fallen.

"I expect he'll come down in the morning to see you off," said Derek, to comfort her.

The tea-party was a merry affair. Mrs. Joyce had made little scones and jam tarts covered with cream. There was fruit salad and fruit cup, and Old Joe played his concertina. Some of the men from out-lying farms dropped in to say good-bye. They sang songs and danced, and Eileen's happiness was completed by the arrival of Daniel.

The party came to an end at last, but Eileen was too weary and full to feel at all sad. Only as Daniel walked home with them, giving her the now customary pick-a-back, did her arms suddenly tighten about his neck.

"What's that for?" he asked.

"Because I'm going to miss you!"

"Well, there is no need to do that for a long time yet."

"Why?"

" Because I am going with you part of the way."

" Really and truly ? " There was gladness in Eileen's voice, and she seized his hand eagerly.

" Yes, really and truly. I've told your mother and she says I'll be most useful."

" Oh, Daniel, I just can't believe it. We'll have such fun ! "

Then in the midst of her pleasure, Daniel saw her face fall, and knowing the reason, hastily interposed.

" It's all settled, Eileen ; I am taking Twink along with me. Now suppose you hurry off to bed—we have an early start in the morning."

The voyage from Burnie to Melbourne was one of continual excitement for Eileen, there was so much novelty in it. John was no sooner on board the ship than he wanted to be allowed to visit the engine-room, and would not stop worrying until Daniel promised him he would try to fix it later. Mrs. Joyce, with her bundles and cases around her, settled herself firmly down. She had a nasty suspicion she was going to be a bad sailor. Twink, wearing his new collar and tied to a rail, looked thoroughly unhappy.

Eileen, for once forgetting Twink, explored every nook and cranny of the vessel ; she climbed into and out of everything. She loved the vastness of the sea, and stood fascinatedly watching the ship ploughing her way through the swirling waters. When they reached Melbourne Daniel took them to the poorer part of the town where they could find lodgings for the night. The large, spacious bungalows standing in their own gardens in the residential area gave her her first glimpse of a luxury of which she had never before been aware. The shops were full of food and clothes in an undreamed-of variety of colours ; and she stared into the windows with such passionate absorption that the crowded throng of well-dressed people looked with interest at the little girl who seemed to have stepped straight out of the backwoods and whose wonderment showed on her face.

" I want to see the town," Eileen confided.

" Then we'll get up early and walk around," Daniel promised, and was as good as his word. The next morning he took the two very excited children up the main streets long before the shops were open, and it was then that Eileen saw something that held her spellbound. They were passing a music shop, and standing alone in its big window was the largest and shiniest black case she had ever seen. She paused and stared at the white ivory keys.

" Daniel, what's that ? "

" What's what ? " He came back good humouredly. " Oh, that's a piano."

" A piano ? "

" Yes; haven't you seen one before ? "

" No. What does it do ? "

" Makes music, like your mouth-organ, but it has more notes and a far sweeter tone."

" Do—do you blow it ? " she asked, looking at him incredulously.

Again he noticed that strange, excited look about

her. "Bless you, no ; you play it with your fingers on those black and white notes. You press them down, like this ! " and he went through the movement of playing on the window-sill. Eileen, standing on tip-toe, watched him closely, then eagerly began to move her fingers in the same way.

"That's it. Gosh, you ought to learn to play the piano one day. You would get more fun out of it than a mouth-organ."

"I can't learn without one of those." She looked at it again, rather wistfully this time. For the first time in her young life she was filled with the wild desire of possession. As other children longed for toys, a doll's pram, a cart, a teddy bear, from that moment she secretly began to long for a piano.

Some time later, when they had boarded another ship and were on their way to Adelaide, Eileen ventured a question.

"Mummie, can you play the piano ? "

"I don't think you could call it that," her mother laughed. "I can strum a few notes. When your father and I were first married there used to be one in a hotel we went to. I picked out a few notes and it used to pass the evenings away."

"I saw one to-day, in a shop."

"But you've seen one before."

"No, I haven't. I should have remembered."

"What a funny child you are." Mrs. Joyce regarded her daughter again with that faintly puzzled expression. "Why all this fuss over a piano ? "

" Do you think I could learn to play one ? "

" What, at your age ?   I never heard of such a thing.
There is a lot you have to learn before that ; besides,
I don't expect there will be any pianos where we are
going.   Lucky if we have a roof over our heads."

" Oh ! "   To hide her disappointment, Eileen
rolled over in her bunk and turned her face to the wall.
For the rest of the journey she never mentioned the
piano again, but her games centred round it.   She
found a hiding-place behind a huge coil of rope under
one of the lifeboats.   There was an old box, and this
became a piano, the one she had seen in the shop
window.   Solemnly she sat before it, fingering and
playing imaginary tunes, utterly and completely happy.

As they steamed down the coast of South Australia,
past the wheat-growing area, the time passed happily
enough for the children, although Mrs. Joyce found
it long and tedious.   It was nearing the end of April
and summer was nearly over.   Daniel was worried,
for with the end of summer would come the wet
season.   He feared the hurricanes, and the heavy,
drenching rains which it would bring.   A bleak
outlook if they were to trek.

A few days before they reached Adelaide a summer
storm of great violence hit the ship.   The lightning
was terrifying in its vividness.   The little ship pitched
and tossed amidst giant waves and cracks of deafening
thunder.   John gave way to tears of utter terror.
Mrs. Joyce was hard put to it to keep her feet and
Twink cowered in a corner.   To Eileen alone the

storm held magic; its sounds excited her, and when at last a lull came, she played the storm all over again on her imaginary piano.

At Adelaide some miners came aboard to work their passage, as Daniel was doing, and at night they would laze on the deck and sing while Daniel would accompany them on his harmonica. Unobserved, Eileen would steal as near as she dared and listen contentedly to the deep, harmonious voices. Once she overheard two of them talking about a " burning mountain." Eileen had never heard of such a thing and went to Daniel with a somewhat anxious expression.

" Daniel, do mountains get on fire in Australia ? "

" No, of course not. Why, there are not even volcanoes."

" But I heard some of the men talking about a ' burning mountain '."

" Oh, that. He meant Mount Wingen on the Liverpool range. It's a queer one, that."

" What makes it burn ? "

" They say there is coal just beneath its surface which gives off gases and causes sort of explosions. It steams and smokes, and do you know how long it has been burning ? "

" How long ? "

" Eight hundred years."

" But that's before you were born ! " Eileen looked a little unbelieving.

" Well, a little," Daniel admitted, and went off highly amused to tell some of the crew.

The days slipped by pleasantly enough, until at last the captain warned Mrs. Joyce that he would have to put them off at his next port of call. " We have to take on extra cargo there," he explained, " but at least you'll be in the west and can get to Kununoppin by land."

" We shall manage all right, Captain," Daniel said, " and mighty glad we have been of your help."

But when the ship docked a few days later at a somewhat isolated port, Daniel began to wonder if their luck would hold, and they would find some form of conveyance. Apart from the port and the storage places for the wheat that was being shipped, there were only a few straggling houses. The hotel showed the only signs of life, and Daniel had a job to fix his charges up for the night. In the morning, however, things looked brighter, for Daniel found a man named Ted who was trekking across the bush, and he somewhat grudgingly agreed to give them all a lift.

CHAPTER IV

A Nasty Experience

EILEEN and John were thrilled with the prospect of a journey by wagon across the bush. They danced around Ted and Daniel excitedly as the two men tried to make some comfort for their journey. Ted eked out a hazardous existence as a carrier between the more lonely bush stations, and his wagon was old and creaked ominously.

"Come on, you kids, fill those sacks with straw, and make a nice big one for your mother. It's the only bed you are going to know for many days," Daniel ordered, and he set them to work with a pile of straw and some good-sized sacks.

This, of course, caused a good deal of merriment, starting with a straw fight, until Eileen managed to push John into the sack he was filling, and hung on to the top so that he couldn't get out. When he did, what began in fun ended in a first-class fight.

"Stop it, you two!" Daniel shouted.

"Eileen, let go of John." Mrs. Joyce knew her daughter's temper and tried to get hold of her, but by now Eileen's nose was bleeding and her fury knew no bounds. She managed to roll John over, and was pressing his face in the mud as hard as she could.

"Daniel, do stop them," pleaded Mrs. Joyce, and Daniel, who could not help laughing at the objects they now presented, managed to get a grip on Eileen, and lifted her, kicking and still fighting, into the air. Without a word he then picked up John also, and with one child under each arm, strode down to the shore.

"Take your clothes off," he ordered sternly, and John, still sobbing ruefully, quickly got out of his. Eileen, still breathing defiance and shooting angry looks at Daniel and John, very reluctantly obeyed.

"Now, into the sea, both of you, and swim it off and get rid of that mud." He chased them in with-

out more ado, while Mrs. Joyce, who had followed, spread out their clothes to dry.

The water was cool and inviting, and in a very few minutes Eileen was racing John through the waves, and shouts of laughter reached the watchers on the shore.

" What a couple ! " sighed Mrs. Joyce, and went back to the wagon to help pack pots and pans.

" Come on out now and finish your job," shouted Daniel, and knowing that he meant it, they came out like lambs and ran up and down the golden sands until they were dry.

" Catch ! " said Daniel, throwing them each a large rosy apple ; and with good will they returned to the sacks and soon had the work completed.

" Pile them up at the end of the wagon," Ted advised. " You can sit on them until you sleep." He loaded up two large kegs of water, for he was taking no risks. Rivers played strange tricks in these parts : they had a habit of being full in one area and completely empty in another.

Kununoppin was a long way off, and although it was Daniel's intention to take the train when they reached the railway, they had some lonely country to go through first. A track had been started from the goldfields of Koolgardie, but it had not yet reached their part of the coast.

Eileen clambered into the wagon, and found a cubby-hole behind a box and quickly fetched some straw.

D

" Twink can sleep here," she said.

" He'd be better in the open air," Daniel warned her.

" Well, not when it rains," argued Eileen, as she showed Twink his new home.

At last everything was ready and the horses harnessed. A few well-wishers gathered to wave them good-bye. A rancher, with whom the children had made friends, slipped something into Eileen's hand and said, " Here's a brownie for you to spend when you get to the end of your journey," and Eileen, looking at it, found a penny. She thanked him shyly, and as they drove off she proudly showed it to Daniel.

" He called it a brownie ; why ? "

" Slang for a penny. You'll hear lots of strange words like that, but you'll soon get to know them. I think we ought to play ourselves out of this town ; come and sit between us."

In spite of a slightly disapproving look from Ted, who had only agreed to their joining the party on condition that he was not to be troubled by the children, Daniel helped Eileen over to the front seat, and so the journey started on a merry note, to the accompaniment of two mouth-organs.

At first it was all new and strange. They were immediately struck by the smallness of the mountains in comparison with those of Tasmania.

" The highest is only 3,000 feet," Daniel explained.

" I shall miss our mountains," Eileen said a little

sadly, and as they pressed on she looked in wonder at the flatness of the country before them; but soon they were exclaiming in delight at some of the wild flowers which grew in abundance, making vivid splashes of colour.

The first time they stopped Eileen gathered a huge armful, and was not content until Daniel had told her some of their names.

"Bless you, child, you seem to think Daniel knows everything," Mrs. Joyce chided.

"Well, he does," Eileen answered quite seriously; and after that Daniel had to give a botany lesson, and try hard to remember the plant names which he had once known so well.

"That's Kangaroo Paw," he said, picking out a delicate white flower. "Look, it's rather like Twink's."

"So it is." Eileen looked at it, fascinated. "And what's this scarlet one?"

"They call that Native Fuchsia. Pretty, isn't it? And those pink flowers are Everlasting Daisies. I tell you what: you can press any new flower you find, and on wet days I'll write the names underneath them for you. In that way you'll know all their names *when* you can read."

"That would be fun," admitted Eileen, and she pestered her mother to show her how to make a book in which to press them out of some old newspapers. This occupation kept both the children engrossed for the next few days, and Mrs. Joyce did all she could to encourage it. When they were out of the wagon they searched for flowers, and when they were in it they pressed and mounted them. There was great excitement when they came upon a magnificent tubular flower such as they had never seen before.

" Daniel, what's this ? " Eileen raced to him eagerly with John hard on her heels.

" That, my child, is the native Tulip or Waratah. It's as symbolic of this country as old Twink is."

" What's symbolic ? " John asked.

" Symbolic ? It means the character or emblem."

" Oh," said John, still not quite understanding.

" The natives used to suck these tubes for the honey that comes out of them. Like this," said Daniel, pulling one off as he did so. " Um—good," he added, and watched the other two as they followed suit and saw their eyes light up with delight at the sweet taste.

That evening as the children slept, Ted wandered off with his pipe and Daniel lazed by the camp fire. Mrs. Joyce asked him one or two questions.

" I can't quite make you out, Daniel ; you seem to know so much."

" Oh, I don't know." Daniel stirred uneasily. " Picked it up, you know."

" Didn't you go to college ? "

" As it happens, I did. I did fairly well at school, and if you do that over here there is every chance of going on to a university even if you haven't any money. I was going to be an engineer ; then I got mixed up with a gold rush and off I went, but my luck was out. I got fed up with it all, and finished up in Tasmania, and you know the rest." He got up slowly, and taking a cloth, helped Mrs. Joyce to wash up.

" I'm almost old enough to be your mother, so you mustn't mind what I am going to say, but I think you are too young to hide yourself up in the mountains and do nothing. Do you mean to go back ? "

" Yes, but it's not quite as bad as that really. You see, just eight years ago, in 1914, I went over to the old country and did my bit of fighting. I got gassed, and am no good for mining any more, or for anything very strenuous. As it happens, I have taken up writing; I write books for children, believe it or not. I suppose that's why I am so interested in them. I think, too, that that's why I am so interested in Eileen; I imagine she is going to do something, that kid."

" Do something ? " Mrs. Joyce looked at him sharply. " It's odd you should say that. Eileen is quite a normal child most of the time, but every now and again she gets this passion for going off by herself, as if—as if she were living in some kind of world in which we have no part."

" I know what you mean," Daniel agreed eagerly. " I've noticed it as well, but I shouldn't worry about it, Mrs. Joyce. Maybe it's all part of the feeling I have about the child, that she will surprise us all sooner or later."

But Mrs. Joyce did worry, and, as it happened, Eileen's passion to wander off by herself did lead to a nasty experience a few days later.

It so happened that one of Australia's fierce and sudden thunderstorms caught them unprepared. They were in pretty thick bush by now, and in parts it was rocky. Daniel and Ted had been uneasy for some days as they had heard the howl of a wolf from time to time. They usually took it in turns, therefore, to keep a good fire burning, but on the night of the storm it had proved impossible. The rain teemed down ; a great tree was struck, and a huge bough fell with a terrifying crash near their camp. The water poured into their wagon through a weak part in the tarpaulin, and the children and Mrs. Joyce spent most of the night mopping up. The storm passed with the same suddenness with which it had come, but everything was running with water and a fire was out of the question.

" I'll take the first watch," Ted said, and patrolled the camp for some hours. A faint moon struggled up, and the storm seemed to have made all wild things restless. In the distance he caught sight of a drove of kangaroos, and as dawn began to break a wild cat sneaked past him, a rabbit in its jaws. A wombat, unaware of his presence, chewed busily at a shrub.

Again came the howl of a wolf. The wombat lifted its heavy, broad head; then with a rolling waddle, looking very much like a cross between a pig and a bear, went off.

" Anything about ? " asked Daniel, who came up at this moment.

" Just heard a wolf again. Must be fairly close, it startled a wombat."

" O.K. I'll keep a look-out. He won't come near unless we annoy him." Daniel lit his pipe and sat down. At that moment he heard a scuffle and quickly picked up his gun, but it was only Twink who had followed him.

" Oh, it's you." Daniel rubbed the animal's head and watched him lazily as Twink began to nibble young shoots. The light increased; nothing stirred, and presently Daniel began to doze. Suddenly he started up with a feeling of impending danger. He looked about him for a moment in a dazed kind of way; then his eyes lighted on Twink, who had wandered a good way off. But it was not Twink that caused him to utter an exclamation of horror, but the sight of a small figure standing near him and watching a large Australian wolf slowly slinking towards them. Unmistakable by its thick head and

truncated muzzle, its yellow body long and slinky and splashed with black stripes, Daniel knew it to be both fierce and determined if attacked. He had seen its species many times at bay, surrounded by a pack of dogs, yet fighting defiantly to the end.

To Daniel's horror, Twink, as if unaware of the threatened danger, ran round Eileen, and she, as if totally unconscious of the ferocity of the wolf, tried to catch her pet. Succeeding, she held Twink by the collar.

"Go away!" Daniel heard her shout in a childish treble.

"Eileen, let Twink go!" shouted Daniel as he raised his rifle; but his warning came too late, for Twink, abruptly aware of his danger, tried to break free, dragging Eileen with him. The kangaroo, beside itself with terror, managed to wriggle free of Eileen's grasp, and doubled back, almost into the jaws of the crouching beast.

"Twink!" wailed Eileen, and ran forward just as the wolf sprang upon its prey.

Daniel saw her check in horror, heard the fierce snarl of the wolf, took aim and with a muttered prayer, fired. To his relief the shot was a lucky one and he saw the long striped body measure its length on the ground, with Twink under it.

"Eileen, you little idiot." His relief gave way to anger as he ran up. He was hardly aware of the white face of the child, but her words soon restored his humour.

" Twink ! Oh, Twink ! He is squashed."

" Squashed indeed ! Lucky it is you are not both dead. What do you mean by wandering about here at this early hour ? " He heaved the body of the wolf off Twink as he spoke, and a very scared kangaroo darted off hurriedly towards the camp.

" I—I missed Twink," Eileen faltered.

" I guess you did." Daniel, who was really blaming himself for what had occurred, picked Eileen up and hugged her tight.

" Listen, kid. Those wolves are nasty and there are a number of them about. Never go wandering about on your own again. Promise ? "

" Yes, Daniel, I promise. I didn't know, truly."

" Well, you do now," said Daniel grimly, and still blaming himself, carried his charge back to the safety of the camp.

It was unfortunate that some days later, when they were once again about to make camp, Eileen, even with the warning Daniel had given her still fresh in her memory, should once again court disaster. They had stopped close to a large area of Malee scrub, which intrigued Eileen so much that she decided to explore it with John. She had never seen anything like it before, for the leaves were matted together overhead like a great umbrella, shutting out the sky.

" Look, John. It's like a great big tent," she cried, peering eagerly into the foliage.

" Let's pretend it's our house," said John, going in under the leaves.

That was quite enough encouragement for Eileen : she was after him in a moment. The ground underneath was clear and barren, and as they went farther they amused themselves climbing in and out of the great stems of the Malee, which branched from the root again and again.

" Let's play hide and seek," said John, and soon the Malee rang with laughter as they surprised each other in the most unexpected places.

" I suppose we had better go back now," Eileen said some time later, as, tired out, they sat down to rest.

" I wish we didn't have to move on quite so fast," grumbled John, as they got reluctantly to their feet.

" This way," said Eileen, stepping out cheerfully in what she thought was the direction of the camp. Five minutes later they both stopped and regarded each other uneasily.

" It's no good you pretending." John stood quite still as he spoke. " We are lost, and you know it."

" Of course we're not lost. Let's call Daniel." Their shouts, however, were met by a heavy silence.

" It must be the other way." In sudden panic they both turned and forced their way through what seemed to them ever-thickening stems. It was John who gave up first, after he had taken a pretty hard toss and hurt his foot.

" It's no good, Ei, it's getting dark ; we're lost."

" Perhaps we had better wait where we are till morning," said Eileen, looking around nervously with the memory of wolves all too fresh in her mind.

Tears were very near, but she was determined not to let John see them.

"I expect there are snakes," John quavered uneasily, "and I'm so thirsty."

"I haven't seen any water anywhere."

"Then we shall die of thirst." John was quite ready to picture the worst.

"We'd better get off the ground. We could sit up there," said Eileen, leading the way to some thick branches which offered some refuge from anything that might be on the prowl. They clambered up and sat close together. The stems were so thick that they presented a natural back which prevented them from falling.

John fell asleep first, but for a long while Eileen stayed awake. At last she fell asleep, and when she awoke it was morning. Quite unexpectedly she began to cry. John awoke also; and tried to cheer her up.

"That won't help," he advised in a fatherly fashion. "Let's have a tune. Got your hurdy-gurdy?"

"Yes," sobbed Eileen, and took it from her pocket, sniffing loudly.

"Go ahead," ordered John briefly, and the music not only cheered them up, but also guided Daniel to them.

The frantic search he and Ted had made all night had got him into the frame of mind to beat Eileen the minute he laid hands on her. When, however, he saw her tear-stained face, and heard her pathetic effort to blow a tune, his resolution left him, and instead he heaved them both down from their perch, and despite their cramped limbs, hurried them back to the camp.

" But we were not far ! " protested poor Eileen in surprise as they came into the clearing.

" Of course you were not far," grumbled Daniel, " but that Malee deadens all sound. That's why you had us up looking for you all night, *and* what about your promise ? "

" I didn't mean to go away, really I didn't." Eileen looked so pathetic that Daniel was hard put to it to be angry any more.

" Oh, what's the use ! " he muttered, and leaving both children to Mrs. Joyce, he went to find Ted and tell him that the children were found. He knew in his heart that it was no good scolding Eileen.

CHAPTER V

Good-bye to Daniel

THE last few days of the journey by wagon proved fairly peaceful. Eileen, a little chastened by her experience in the Malee and the fact that John had developed a temperature as a result, became Daniel's shadow and did not wander any more. One evening they came upon a river and camped close to its cool banks. Eileen, of course, wanted to swim, so Daniel good naturedly accompanied her. It was almost dusk, and after the heat of the day and dust of the journey, Eileen just revelled in the coolness of the water on her skin.

"Eileen!" She heard Daniel almost whisper her name, and, turning, saw him beckoning to her. She swam gently to the bank, hardly making a sound.

"What's the matter?" she whispered.

"Look over there!"—he pointed to the bank lower down on the far side—"there's a platypus."

"What a funny looking object. Whatever is it?"

"That funny little object has caused more interest than any other animal to scientific men," said Daniel, half seriously.

"But it looks like a bit of everything," said Eileen, as well she might, for it presented the strangest appearance. About two feet long, its fur was thick and soft, and its feet were webbed; it had long claws with which it was busy burrowing with terrific force through some soft earth. Its tail was like a beaver's, yet its body was not unlike a mole's. To crown all, it had a huge flat beak exactly like a duck's.

"It's the only mammal known to lay eggs," Daniel whispered as they watched it. "And it lives underground just as happily as in the water. You are lucky to see it, kid. There are all sorts of people who would give a great deal for the sight of one."

"I wish we could take it with us!"

"I think Twink is enough, and it wouldn't like captivity."

At that moment the platypus entered the water and swam off. As they walked back to the camp, Daniel

related how he had once had the luck to see some young ones.

"They reminded me of kittens playing together. They rolled over and over on the ground and knocked each other over. They don't see very well in the daylight, and their eyes are so wide apart that they are not able to focus anything directly in front of them. They'll bump into anything that gets in their way and sit there looking so offended.'"

"What silly things! They don't seem to know quite what they are, do they, Daniel?"

"You've said it," he agreed laughingly.

All too soon those happy, carefree days with Daniel came to an end. Eileen was dismayed as the time of parting drew near. Daniel was so interested in everything, so ready to answer all her questions. Little did Eileen realize it then, but he had awakened in her a desire to learn about all sorts of things, and, above all, a craving for music. Now, as he stood by the train that was to take them the last part of the journey to Kununoppin, Eileen stood beside him overwhelmed by a feeling of desolation.

"You are sure you won't come on with us?" Mrs. Joyce was saying. "My husband will want to thank you personally for all your help."

"Much as I would like to, I must make my way to Perth. Since I am here, I want to fix up with a publisher, and you will be safe enough now. Twink is quite all right in the guard's van, young 'un," and he looked down at Eileen. "Oh, come now," for he saw a big tear overflow and splash down her cheek. Without a word he picked her up and carried her aboard the train. "This is not good-bye; when you least expect it I shall turn up to see you."

"Will you, Daniel? I—I shall miss you dreadfully!"

"Yes, I'm afraid you are going to be that kind of person," Daniel said, more to himself than to her. "What you've got to do now is learn to read and write. Then we can exchange letters and tell each other all sorts of things; and don't forget I shall expect lots of new tunes on that mouth-organ when we next meet. Come on, give me a kiss and let's see you smile." He put his finger under her chin and grinned at her cheerfully. "Silly little coon, aren't you?" and quite suddenly they both began to laugh as they had at their first meeting. The last sight Daniel had of Eileen was as she leant out of the window waving to him frantically, shouting that she would see him soon.

Fortunately, there was a new excitement in the thought of seeing her father. The journey seemed long enough, but there was plenty to look at. They passed through great areas where herds of cattle grazed, and once a large herd of kangaroo amused them by trying to race the train. Some friendly Australians gave the children pineapples and oranges, and explained that they grew not so very far away.

"We shan't be long now," Mrs. Joyce told them at last, and Eileen looked with interest at the great timber forests which supplied the miners with the wooden props they needed.

As the train ran into Kununoppin, both children craned out of the window, eager to get their first glimpse of their new home.

" Will Uncle be here ? " John asked.

" I shouldn't think so," answered Mrs. Joyce. " It was quite impossible to let him know when to expect us "; but again Daniel's forethought had preceded them, for a telegram, sent directly the train was out of sight, caused Mr. Joyce to be pacing the station anxiously. He caught sight of the children first and shouted a welcome to them.

" He is there, Mummie ! " Eileen cried excitedly, and soon there was a scramble to get out of the train and rush at him. Eileen stood by a little shyly while her mother and father greeted each other, but soon it was as if they had never been parted. There was so much to tell that they all tried to talk at once.

" You have both grown," said Mr. Joyce, regarding the children approvingly; but he looked a little shaken when Twink was produced from the guard's van.

" Whatever made you bring him ? " He looked disapprovingly at his wife.

" The child has adored that animal ever since you gave him to her ; we had to bring him."

" I was going to leave him with Daniel," Eileen explained.

" Who may Daniel be ? " Mr. Joyce asked as he

E

helped his family up into a cart which he had borrowed, and as they drove some way out of the town, Eileen told her father all about their friend and Mrs. Joyce explained how helpful he had been.

"I am afraid things are not too good here." Mr. Joyce spoke seriously to his wife. "We've been prospecting a new seam and things have not worked according to plan." He looked at her a little uneasily.

"But you promised not to send for us until things were better."

"Yes, I know. We thought we had struck a rich seam, but it ended in disappointment. You know how these things are?"

"Yes, I know how they are!" Mrs. Joyce sighed deeply. It was not much fun being a miner's wife, especially a miner who liked his own independence and preferred to work his own claim rather than be employed by someone else. She was not surprised to find that their new home consisted of a couple of tents and very little comfort. There was always the chance that soon their luck would change and that there would be better days. But it was two hard years before Mr. Joyce admitted defeat and they decided to make a move.

Meanwhile, John took to the life like a duck to water. He enjoyed the company of the other boys in the camp. He liked to help his uncle and he was not a bit homesick for Tasmania. With Eileen it was different. She missed her mountains and lakes, and, above all, she missed Daniel. Everything seemed so different. The miners were friendly enough, but they were rough folk, and when work was finished they would gather together in the only hotel, making a lot of noise, talking and arguing. At times the talking would turn to fighting and then everything would be in an uproar. Eileen hated the fights. It was one thing for her to get the best of John if she thought it necessary, but she hated the sight of angry men fighting with bare fists, and if she was near when one began she would run away and hide. Sometimes her father would come and find her and, taking her back, he would tell her not to be silly.

"They don't mean anything," he laughed. "It's just high spirits. I think it's time you went to school instead of hanging around doing nothing. I'll talk to your mother."

The result of the talk was that Eileen found herself trudging a good many miles to a little school in the bush. Her first reception was not good. The school was kept by a sour-faced teacher who hated teaching, but did it because she had an old father to keep and had to do something to bring in some money.

"Got your sixpence?" She glared at Eileen over the top of her pince-nez with marked disapproval. All she saw was another miner's child, poorly clad, with not even a pair of shoes. She quite failed to see that here was a very sensitive little girl, quite eager to learn.

"No," faltered Eileen, under the unfriendly stare.

" Why not ? " rapped Miss Blenheim.

" My Mummie hadn't got one."

There was a titter from behind her back and she felt a hot flush spread over her face. The lack of money had never worried Eileen before, but here it seemed to gather importance.

" Very well ; until you bring it you will sit on the back bench with the others of your kind," Miss Blenheim answered viciously. She was unable to refuse education, but she resented having to give it for nothing.

" Thank you," said Eileen, without meaning to be rude, and turned to go to her place.

" And don't be pert. I'll show you what happens to little girls who are pert ! " and Miss Blenheim rose to her feet in fury and picked up a cane from her desk.

" Hold out your hand," she snapped.

Quite unaware of what was to befall her, Eileen did as she was told. The next moment she received a stinging blow across her palm, then another and another. It was the first time Eileen had ever been hit with a stick and her first inclination was to cry out. Then somehow she knew that this would give her tormentor great satisfaction, and although she went very white, not a sound escaped her.

" Now go to your place," Miss Blenheim said.

So, pressing her hand hard against her side because it burnt, Eileen walked to the back of the class and joined seven little girls who seemed to be looking at her with sympathy.

She soon learnt why in the days that followed, for they, with her, ranked as paupers in Miss Blenheim's eyes. It was only those miners' children who could afford their sixpences and others who came from out-lying farms that she smiled upon. All her bad temper was focused upon the back benchers. She gave them no books, only odd bits of paper on which to learn to write. Fortunately for Eileen, there was another child named Doris who seemed to have earned Miss Blenheim's dislike even more than she had.

Doris was meek and undersized; so nervous that she found it quite impossible to answer any questions. This so infuriated Miss Blenheim that day after day her stick would come down on the wretched child's body. The class would watch, thrilled with horror, afraid they would also suffer the same fate if any of them made a protest.

Then one day things came to a head. Eileen, in spite of Miss Blenheim's lack of interest, had been able to answer many questions which the rest of the class had failed to do, and for the first time the teacher had vouchsafed her a few wintry words of praise; but the next moment Doris had upset her with some par-ticularly stupid answer. Miss Blenheim screeched at her for lack of attention, then swooped down upon the unfortunate child. She began to belabour her with all the will in the world, and suddenly Eileen could endure it no longer. A fury at the injustice of it all; the memory of Doris, with whom she had walked back from school, sobbing that she was going to run away, came upon her in a flash. She didn't stop to think; her temper was up. She hurled herself upon Miss Blenheim with all the strength of her young body. She clung on to the arm that was wielding the stick, shouting in her anger, " Stop it ! Stop it, you beast ! "

Doris, in the struggle, went hurtling to the floor and lay strangely still and white, while Miss Blenheim, now beside herself with rage, tried to shake off the clinging Eileen. This was too much for the class— they rose to their feet and started to cheer.

" Go it, Eileen ! "

" Get the stick, Eileen ! "

" Go on, Eileen ! "

Eileen, nothing loth, wrenched the stick from the teacher's hand, and her eyes blazing, her breath coming in gasps, she jumped on it and broke it in halves.

" That will teach you ! " she almost sobbed. Then, utterly spent, she turned and ran from the school, and kept on running until she reached home. It was Twink she went to then. Releasing him from the pen her father had made for him, she slipped off again and walked with her pet until her anger died down and she began to wonder what would happen. One thing was plain. Miss Blenheim would not have her in the school again. This would anger her father, for he would not know the real reason—the teacher would see to that. Just then she came upon John, who was busy fishing in a very narrow stream. Sitting down beside him, she confided the whole story.

" Stop it !   Stop it, you beast ! "

(*See page* 70)

" I can't think why you go to school," he reasoned. Education not being compulsory outside towns, John had got round his uncle not to send him. " Do you like it ? "

" Not very much," admitted Eileen, " but I like the lessons. I can write now."

" What will you want with writing ? " scoffed John.

" It's fun making letters."

" It's more fun to be able to play around. Anyway, you'll be able to now. You can come out with me to-morrow," he suggested by way of making up to her ; then he laughed suddenly. " Good for you, Eileen. I'm glad you gave that old frump what for ; but I shouldn't go near her again."

Eileen, however, did not follow his advice, for when, after three days of pretending not to feel well she was sent for by Miss Blenheim, she went without a word. Jean, who had called for her, was not very comforting.

" I expect the old girl is out for your blood," she said, with a sidelong glance.

" What happened—after I had gone ? "

" She was shaking like a leaf. She told us all to go home, and she said that if we said anything about what had happened she would give us all the stick. Funny thing is, she hasn't hit any of us since. P'raps she was scared. Doris had sort of fainted, and the old girl picked her up and took her into her house. She has been quite nice to her since."

" I expect I shall get it all," said Eileen.

" We are all on your side."

With these comforting words in her ears, Eileen entered the school. She expected Miss Blenheim to call her, but nothing happened. When the time came for them to go, Eileen still expected to be told to stay behind. Miss Blenheim, however, completely ignored her, and then it was Eileen realized that no reference was to be made to what had passed. Had she but known it, the fury of one child had so shocked Miss Blenheim into the knowledge of the hatred she had aroused that it had brought her to her senses. From then on, school life became passably pleasant. True, they were stung by Miss Blenheim's tongue, but not so often by her cane. There was a kind of armed neutrality of which Eileen took full advantage. She eagerly learned all that the mistress cared to teach her.

Things were not always easy at home. Her parents tried to keep a cheerful countenance, but it was a thin time for them all. A pioneer's life is never easy in a young country, especially when new ground has to be broken, fresh gold searched for, and though there was always hope, there was often heart-break. It was a comfortless, hard existence, and at times her mother gave way to tears of utter weariness.

The time came when Mr. Joyce realized that somehow he must see his family better housed. He could not go on waiting and working for that streak of gold that would all of a sudden enable them to have all the comfort they wanted.

" We are going to Boulder City," he announced one evening.

" Is it a real city ? " Eileen asked excitedly.

" You'll soon see," her father answered. " I shall work in the mines there," he told his wife briefly, and went out to hide his disappointment.

CHAPTER VI

Boulder City

TRUE to his word, Mr. Joyce took his family to Boulder City, and it was a happy change for them. How great a change it was to mean to Eileen none of them had the least inkling. The only thing that concerned Eileen herself for the moment was that, after a somewhat difficult scene with her father, she still had Twink with her. The journey having strained their purse very greatly, they were fortunate in finding a rather dilapidated bungalow in the poorer part of the town. At least it had a roof and floorboards upon which to walk, and Mrs. Joyce felt that nothing else mattered very much. There were plenty of shops and good food to be had as soon as things looked up. The city was close to the " Gold Mile," the richest gold mine in the world. It was full of miners and their families, and each year saw some improvement in social conditions. Most of the bungalows were lighted by electricity, and water was brought to the city from three hundred miles away.

For the first few weeks John and Eileen spent a great deal of time exploring. The lights at night thrilled them, and the air of companionship about the place was comforting. They had not been there long before neighbours dropped in offering help ; and boxes and odd chairs with which to furnish the home were soon forthcoming.

" Just oddments until you can buy some furniture," a neighbour would say, for many of them had known bad patches themselves.

John got busy with nails and hammer—he was quite a handy carpenter—and Eileen helped her mother scrub out the bungalow and make it more homelike. Fortunately, there was a ramshackle old shed in the so-called garden, and Twink was allowed this as his home. Every morning Eileen took him out into the open spaces in search of young shoots for him to eat. She caused a good deal of amusement among the miners as she solemnly walked along with Twink, now confined to a collar and chain, always close beside her ; but he quickly made her many friends, and the difficulty of feeding was soon overcome, for the men would drop titbits over the fence for him as they went home. But Eileen's days of freedom were numbered ; before long the priest called on Mrs. Joyce, and it was arranged that John and Eileen should go to the convent school.

" But I don't want to go," she argued with her mother, memories of her last school looming before her.

" This time you have to go." Mrs. Joyce sounded quite firm. Sooner or later she must buy her daughter some clothes, she thought, but it was out of the question just then.

The next day Mrs. Joyce took John and Eileen to

the gates of the school. Children were flocking in from all parts of the city, some well dressed, some as poorly clad as Eileen. This was a far bigger school than the one she had been to before, and she suddenly felt shy. She felt shyer still when she first saw the Sisters. They were dressed unlike anything she had seen before, and she stared in wonderment. Never had she seen anyone clothed in such long, flowing garments, or with so much of themselves covered up.

" What is your name ? " one of them asked her kindly.

" Eileen Joyce."

" Well, Eileen, here is a nice new copy-book for you, and you may go and sit over there," and Sister Veronica pointed to a form not very far back. The morning passed pleasantly enough, and was very different from her experiences with Miss Blenheim. She had her first lesson in painting, and enjoyed mixing her colours and getting paint over everything ; but it was not until she had been some days at school that the miracle happened. She had been sent to fetch something for Sister Veronica from the

building where the Sisters lived across the garden. As she neared the entrance the sound of music caught her ears. She paused and realized that it was coming from an open window. Quickly she went towards it, and very cautiously pulling herself up on tip-toe, she peeped in. A little gasp escaped her, for inside the room was a piano. A girl was playing, and the notes were clear and sweet, unlike anything Eileen had ever heard before. It seemed that a lesson was in progress, for the next moment a Sister spoke, and taking the girl's place, played over the same tune. Eileen was simply entranced. She quite forgot her errand; in fact, she forgot everything—everything but the piano and the lovely, exciting sounds it made.

In her eagerness to see and hear more Eileen put her foot on a small ledge, and in an effort to pull herself up higher, she slipped.

"Who is there?" The playing ceased, and the Sister, coming to the window, saw the excited face of the child.

"What are you doing there?" she continued sternly.

"Please—I was listening."

"Why are you

not in school ? Come back and see me after lessons. I want an explanation."

" Yes, Sister." Somewhat dashed, Eileen went to the entrance, found the book she had been told to fetch from the hall and hurried back to the class.

Alas, more trouble awaited her ! Where had she been ? What had she done ? Her failure to answer to both questions resulted in three strokes of the cane. After all, how could she explain to Sister Veronica that she had heard a piano and just had to go to it ?

Later in the morning, as they all streamed out of class, with some misgiving, Eileen found her way back towards the music room. She was not sure of the way, so she went and stood in full view of the window, wondering then why she had come. The Sister did not know her name and might have forgotten the incident ; but Eileen knew that really she had come to see the piano—not in obedience to the command.

Sister Augustine soon caught sight of the small figure. " What are you standing there for ? I told you to come to me. Come round by the door," she called.

With beating heart Eileen went in, and seeing an open door, approached it. She tapped softly and entered the presence—not the presence of Sister Augustine, but the presence of the Piano. Her eyes flew to it at once and she hardly heard the Sister's first words.

" Now perhaps you will tell me what you were

doing climbing up on my window-sill during a lesson ?
In fact, at any time.''

'' I—I wanted to listen.''

'' To listen ! '' Sister Augustine sounded quite
startled at this perfectly simple explanation.

'' Yes. Please, will you teach me to play ? ''
There was a boldness about Eileen now ; she was
quite unaware that she was in disgrace. Her hand
stole out and ran caressingly over the piano frame.

Sister Augustine watched her in astonishment.
She had never seen such strange behaviour before.
She suddenly realized that Eileen was quite unaware of
why she had been sent for.

'' What is your name ? '' she asked in a gentler tone.

'' Eileen—Eileen Joyce.''

'' You are new here ? ''

'' Yes.'' Eileen dragged her eyes from the piano
and smiled one of her quick, friendly smiles.

'' Are you fond of music ? ''

'' I—I don't know.'' Eileen looked at her ques-
tioner a little helplessly. '' But I would like to play
the piano.''

'' Well, you are a strange child.'' Sister Augustine
sat down and drew Eileen towards her. Little by
little she extracted from Eileen some of her history
and all about the mouth-organ.

'' Have you got it with you ? '' she asked with
interest.

'' Yes.'' Eagerly Eileen took her treasure from her
pocket.

"Give me a tune." Quite unaware of why the child had roused her interest, Sister Augustine sat back and listened.

"Well, you certainly can play a mouth-organ, and you seem to have music in you."

"Oh, thank you."

"I am afraid you will have to ask your mother for an extra sixpence. You see, it is a rule that music lessons must be paid for."

"Oh!" Eileen's joy at the promise of lessons died.

"Is that going to be very difficult?" Sister Augustine asked.

"I don't know," Eileen answered truthfully.

F

She hoped that perhaps her mother would be able to give it to her.

"Then come back to me when you have got it." Sister Augustine dismissed her kindly, determined to question Sister Veronica about her.

In a haze of hope and doubt, Eileen ran home as fast as her legs could carry her.

"Mummie, the music teacher will give me piano lessons if I take her sixpence!" She spoke so fast that Mrs. Joyce for the moment could hardly gather what she said.

"Sixpence! Sixpence for what? The Father said your education would cost nothing!"

"For music lessons!"

"Eileen! I've told you before, it is out of the question. Even if I could spare it now, it would only be the first of many. Each time we would have to pay, and even if I did not think it sheer lunacy, I just can't afford it."

"But, Mummie, I want to learn!" Eileen stamped her foot angrily. In this she was quite unreasonable. She only knew it was the most important thing that had ever happened to her.

"There are so many things we want, Eileen, and we just have to do without them. Shoes, for instance."

"But I want to play. I will play!"

"Now don't get in a temper with me. What has come over you, child? As a rule you are so understanding."

" Yes, but this is different. I—I think you are horrid ! "

" It's just some silly nonsense Daniel has put into your head, and the sooner you get it out the better." Mrs. Joyce was annoyed herself now. " Go out and get some wood and let me hear no more of it."

" I won't and I shan't." Furiously Eileen went out and slammed the door. She was desperately disappointed, but over this she did not cry. She was filled, instead, with a grim determination that somehow, in her own way, she would get that sixpence.

When she returned to the bungalow she had quite recovered. Mrs. Joyce, for her part, was sorry that she had not shown more understanding. When she tucked Eileen up that night she sat down on her bed.

" I'm sorry about the money. I would give it to you if I could spare it."

" It doesn't matter now." Eileen sounded detached.

Her mother felt shut out from her confidence. " I know what we'll do. As to-morrow is Saturday you shall come down to your uncle's hotel. He has a piano there. I'll show you how to press the notes."

" Will you ? "

Mrs. Joyce was rewarded when her daughter sat up in her excitement.

" Yes ; you'll enjoy that much more than silly old lessons."

" Yes," agreed Eileen ; but after her mother had left her she snuggled down and smiled happily to herself. Something had given her an idea of how to raise that sixpence and nobody was going to stop her. In one thing she was quite determined. She was going to have lessons and she was going to pay for them herself. The next morning Mrs. Joyce made a great effort to get everything done early ; then, calling Eileen, they set off for the hotel.

" One day we will have one of these." She pointed to the neat little bungalows built from timber or sheeting in which many of the miners were housed. It was a cheerful, busy morning, and the main streets were full of activity. Everyone was friendly and passed the time of day.

" That's where your uncle lives," said Mrs. Joyce, pointing to a long low hotel made of timber. Outside there was a rail where horses could be tethered, for the hotel was a favourite haunt of the miners.

" Well, this is a surprise ! " Eileen's uncle, who was busy sweeping up, greeted Mrs. Joyce warmly. " So this is young Eileen ? Got a kiss for your uncle ? '' Eileen submitted meekly, wiping it off rather too obviously as soon as his back was turned.

'' I promised the child I would show her your piano.''

'' You can hardly call it a piano, Alice, but there it is.'' He pointed to a dilapidated object, stained with beer marks and with half the ivory chipped off the keys. '' Is the kid musical ? '' He looked at his niece with interest.

'' She has some strange notion that she wants to learn to play the piano. I promised to show her how to play the notes.''

'' Go right ahead. I'll get you a cup of tea,'' and he left them and went into the back kitchen.

'' Now, Eileen ! '' Mrs. Joyce turned to speak to her daughter, but she was already standing before the piano. There was such a stillness about her that for a moment Mrs. Joyce did not move. She watched her instead as, very slowly, Eileen extended her hand and softly, almost reverently, pressed down a note. Her touch was so light that there was no response. She turned and looked at her mother.

'' Look, like this,'' and Mrs. Joyce sat down and played a few notes.

'' Let me try.'' All eagerness, Eileen did the same. '' Show me some more,'' she begged.

'' I can't show you much. This is how you play an exercise. It's called the five-finger exercise, and it's the only one I know,'' laughed her mother, and with stiff fingers she played up and down. That was quite enough for Eileen. She set to with a will, her face flushed with the intensity of her concentration, the notes groaning and creaking with age as she played them.

" Seems we have a young pianist in the family," her uncle laughed. "When she grows up she can come and play for the boys."

" She's quick at picking up things," Mrs. Joyce explained, content that Eileen would now perhaps be satisfied.

" Let the kid come and tinkle about if she's as keen as all that."

" Do you hear that, Eileen ? " Mrs. Joyce called. " Your Uncle says you may come and play here sometimes."

" Oh, thank you—may I really ? " She shot her uncle a look of gratitude.

" We must go now," said Mrs. Joyce, immediately after tea, but it was some minutes before she could get Eileen away from the piano. At last her uncle went over, and picking her up, began to tickle her. This so enraged Eileen that she wriggled free and ran out of the building.

" That's a strange kid, Alice ; she is really wild." He scratched his head in perplexity.

" Don't take any notice. I don't know what comes over her when it has anything to do with music. She's quite unreasonable."

" Perhaps you have a budding genius ! " and, well pleased with his joke, her brother-in-law went off into fits of laughter.

Mrs. Joyce was annoyed, and she scolded Eileen most of the way home for her bad manners.

" Serve you right if he doesn't let you play again."

" Oh, he will, won't he ? " Touched at last, Eileen took notice of what her mother was saying.

" I don't know. I really don't understand you." Thoroughly put out, Mrs. Joyce set about getting the dinner when they reached home. Eileen hovered about her, and at last she spoke.

" I'm sorry. I was thinking of the notes, and when he tickled me I got mad."

" Oh, very well." Mrs. Joyce gave her daughter a piece of pastry just to show she was no longer angry.

That evening Eileen made her way with Twink towards her uncle's hotel. She did not go inside, for it was very crowded and she was not sure of her welcome. Instead she sat on the side of the steps close to where some men were lounging.

" Hi, little girl, you had better run off home," one of them said.

" I've come to see my uncle." Eileen smiled in her most friendly fashion.

" Who is your uncle ? " another asked.

" The owner of this hotel," she said, with some importance.

" Shall I fetch him ? " the first speaker asked.

" No, he will come when he is ready. Shall I give you a tune ? " and she took out her mouth-organ.

" Oh, we don't want no kids' noises here," one of them said ; but by then Eileen had started to play.

One or two of the others drew near, and soon she had a small party round her and a few voices joined in.

" The kid's good ! " one of them laughed good-naturedly. " Here, catch," and he threw her a penny. " That's for luck." His example was followed by another, and Eileen, well pleased with her plan, began to play again. Unfortunately, at that moment, when finances were looking up, her uncle came out to see whence the music was coming. When he saw his niece he could hardly believe his eyes. He did not see the pennies because Eileen had picked them up, but he felt his brother would not be best pleased to hear that his daughter was giving entertainment on his steps.

" Now then, Eileen, what's all this ? "

" I—I came to say I was sorry I ran out this morning without saying thank you," and Eileen disarmed him with a charming smile.

" That's all right, child, but now you had better run home. You can come in the mornings when we are closed."

" Thank you, Uncle." Well pleased with herself, she went home, clutching the two pennies in a somewhat hot hand. She went straight to Twink's shed and hid them in a box which she put on a ledge. As she came out she noticed that the boy next door was staring in her direction, but she didn't give it a thought. She felt extremely elated. She had two whole pennies towards the music lessons, and nothing else mattered.

CHAPTER VII

Music Lessons at Last

EILEEN was up early the next morning, too early for the boy next door, and as she went outside she saw him slip into Twink's shed. Eileen never had liked him ; he had a squint and his nose was always running. His name was Percy, and once he had thrown a stone at Twink, and because she had called him names for doing so, he had twisted her arm. He was bigger than she, but very thin, and his legs were rather bandy.

" How dare he ! " Thinking he was going to tease Twink, she hurried very softly to the shed, and was just about to enter when she met Percy coming out. She got in his way and pushed him back.

" What are you doing with Twink ? "

" Nothin'. Get out of my way ! " The boy looked alarmed, so alarmed that Eileen guessed he had been up to something. Her eyes wandered to her tin box. It was on the ledge, but the lid was by its side. Quite unexpectedly she pushed Percy with all her might. He was taken by surprise so that he fell over backwards. While he measured his length on the ground, she picked up the box and looked in. The pennies were gone !

"You beastly little thief!" Once again she was seized with unreasoning rage. Her two pennies! Her two pennies towards her lessons! With one thought only in her mind—to get them back—she flung herself at him just as he was getting up.

"Give me my pennies!" She beat on his chest with clenched fists.

"I haven't got your pennies!" Percy endeavoured to throw her off.

"Yes, you have." Eileen tried to reach his pocket as she sat on him, but he exerted all his strength, and in a moment they were fighting in good earnest. She got hold of his hand and bit it hard; with a yell of rage Percy wriggled away, and in doing so, the pennies rolled to the ground. They made a dart at them together, and Eileen's head hit Percy full in the eye. This made him savage, and he hit Eileen as hard as he knew how, then proceeded to pull her hair. At this Eileen started to kick. She was beside herself with fury. She caught him on the shin bone and he went down like a ninepin, and following up her advantage, she flung herself at him again.

"I'll teach you to touch anything of mine," she almost cried, for there was a nasty scratch on her face and it hurt.

It was upon this scene that her father fortunately came, for Eileen was by then getting the worst of it. For a moment he paused in surprise, then in a second had dragged them apart, and to their feet, shaking them both extremely hard.

"Eileen! How dare you behave like this! Percy, what are you doing here? Look at you both!" They did indeed look a sorry sight. Percy's eye was swollen and almost closed. Eileen's face was bleeding, her frock was torn.

"He took something of mine." Eileen pushed her hair out of her eyes and glared at the offending Percy. She could not help the feeling of satisfaction that he could not see out of his eye.

"No, I didn't."

"Yes, you did."

"What did he take?" Mr. Joyce asked.

"Er—something." Caution warned Eileen not to say what. Her father would want to know how she came by two pence and what it was for.

"Well, I'm disgusted with you both. Eileen, go

to your mother. I will punish you later. Percy, go home, and don't let me catch you over here again."

Percy decided this was the moment to start howling as he made his way through the fence back to his parents.

Eileen, with an

anxious look at her pennies lying in the corner, but not daring to pick them up, ran indoors.

" Gracious, child, what have you been up to ? " Mrs. Joyce seized her daughter and began to bathe her face.

" The child has been fighting with young Percy," Mr. Joyce said, as he came in.

" There must have been some reason ? " Mrs. Joyce knew that Eileen rarely got fighting mad. " What was it, Eileen ? "

But Eileen would not say, and her father got angry at her silence. At that moment there was a knock at the door, and Percy's infuriated mother entered dragging her reluctant son by the hand.

" Look at his eye ! Look at it ! That wretched child of yours set on him for nothing ! "

That was quite enough for Mrs. Joyce. She was quick in Eileen's defence, and there were very angry words between the women before Mrs. Pratt took herself off with the snivelling Percy.

" The child must be taught that she cannot fight," said her father. " She will not go out to-day, and is to have nothing but bread and water. I won't have it, Eileen ; you are getting too big to behave this way."

Poor Eileen ! It was a bad day for her. She had hoped to make some more pennies, and when John came in she confided the whole story to him.

" Will you get my pennies for me ? " she begged.

" All right, but I think you ought to give me one."

" Please, John, I want them so badly."

"I'll think about it," said John, but in a little while he brought the pennies to her. "Don't worry, Eileen; Percy isn't going to get away with a thing like this. I'll set the gang on to him."

He was as good as his word, for the next morning, on the way to school, Eileen saw an extremely dilapidated Percy climbing out of the horse trough, while vanishing round the corner were a number of other small boys. The day proved as good as the Sunday had been bad, for when she was playing marbles in front of a Mrs. Swift's gate after school, the old lady came out and called to her. She wanted some potatoes fetched from the near-by store, and when Eileen brought them back she invited her in.

"Here's a penny for your trouble." Mrs. Swift fumbled in her purse and produced a lovely shining copper.

"No—no, thank you," said Eileen, and only she knew the effort it cost her to refuse; but she was a generous child and liked to do things for people.

"I insist, child. Not for fetching the potatoes, but because I know little girls like bright pennies."

"Well, I do really." Still Eileen hesitated.

"Then take it." Since Mrs. Swift was so insistent, Eileen thankfully accepted, hardly able to believe that fortune had so favoured her.

"Now let's have a cup of tea." The old lady fetched the tea-pot from the hob, and soon Eileen was chatting to her happily, especially when she found that Mrs. Swift had once lived in Tasmania.

" Yes, my dear, I came over here as a bride. It was very different then—they were wild times. Men shot each other for gold—greedy they were, greedy for it." She shook her head sadly, for her husband, who became sheriff of the town, had lost his life very early in just such a skirmish.

" It doesn't seem to do them much good, looking for it," Eileen said, thinking of what Daniel had said, and also of her father's fruitless search.

" It gets into their blood; they go on and on. Don't you ever marry a miner. You are young yet, but remember an old woman's words when you grow up." Then, as if realizing for the first time that she was talking to a child, she smiled, for Eileen was looking quite serious.

" There, now, how I do go on ! Let's see if I've got any sweets in this tin." She fetched a tin down from the dresser, and with very old fingers, fished one out. Eileen stared, fascinated, for she imagined that Mrs. Smith must be over a hundred years old; but she liked her, and enjoyed being talked to as if she were grown up. It was the beginning of many visits. Eileen would sit enthralled while Mrs. Swift told her stories of the days when she was young; of the great forests that were felled to allow for buildings and the growth of the mines; of the mad rush for gold when it was first discovered; of the boom that followed, and the people who came from all over the world; of the terrible hardship from lack of water, and the bringing of it through pipes from three hundred miles away.

" It must be tired when it comes out of the tap,''
Eileen remarked thoughtfully at this information.

It was at Mrs. Swift's that Eileen used to write to
Daniel. She had told the old lady all about him, and
shyly took any letters she received from him for her
to read. It seemed that he had made some money
writing a book, and he promised to send Eileen a
copy. He asked what she was doing about her music.
This interested Mrs. Swift, who questioned her very
closely.

It was soon after this that Eileen ventured to collect
some more pennies. This time she did not go down
to her uncle's, but one very hot evening after school
she took Twink to the outskirts of the city. There
was a large tree with seats all round it, and here the
men often used to sit. She knew some of them, and
was soon talking to one particular friend named Dick.

" Look what I've got." She showed him the
mouth-organ.

" Gosh, I used to have one of those. Can you
play it ? '' Dick was young and very bored; anything was welcome that broke the monotony of life.

" Yes, I'll play it." Eileen started up, and soon
she had the men singing with her. Then one of them
wanted to play a tune himself. That was an anxious
moment, and Eileen never took her eyes off the
precious instrument until it was back in her hands.
She played one more tune as the men began to
disperse, well pleased with their sing-song.

" Can you do with a brownie ? '' One of them

Three more halfpennies dropped at her feet.

(See page 98)

flicked a penny towards her. Another, amused, chucked a halfpenny.

"Thank you, kind sir," she said, quoting a bit of a poem she had learnt at school and dropping him a curtsy. This tickled someone else, and three more halfpennies dropped at her feet.

Eileen could hardly believe her luck. She collected the precious coins and ran home on winged feet. The next morning she was at school before the bell even began to ring. She rushed straight over to the music room, but Sister Augustine was not there. During class she lost marks for inattention, and the moment the bell went for break she rushed off again. Sister Augustine was just leaving for her lunch.

"Please, I've got it!"

"Got what?" For a moment Sister Augustine was slightly taken aback. She could not think to what this starry-eyed child was referring. It had been some time since their first conversation.

"Sixpence!" In triumph Eileen displayed the money.

"For lessons?" Sister Augustine remembered in a flash. This was the child so anxious to learn to play the piano. "Well done! I thought you had forgotten all about it; but I am afraid you will have to wait until next term now, dear."

"Next term?" There was such despair in Eileen's voice that Sister Augustine, who was just about to hurry on, came back and put her arm round Eileen's shoulders.

" My dear child, it's not so very long. You have forgotten that we break up in a week."

" Oh. Oh, I see. Thank you." Eileen turned and walked down the passage, and Sister Augustine, watching her, thought she had never seen anyone so disconsolate. Then and there she made a note in her book that Eileen should have her first lesson the very first day of the next term.

Eileen never knew how she got through those holidays. It was the most tantalizing time in the whole of her life. To have the sixpence at last and then have to wait ! She became listless and broody.

" Reminds me of a pricked bubble," her father said anxiously one evening to his wife.

" Do you think she is brooding, Joseph, because she can't have her music lessons ? "

" No, it can't matter at that age as much as that. I don't understand this craze, but, then, kids do get queer notions."

" She is temperamental, and she does fret about things sometimes. She is quite different from John."

" I expect the kid is run-down. Living in tents didn't help any of you."

Meanwhile, the cause of this anxious discussion was confronted with yet another problem. It so happened that a famous pianist was visiting Boulder City. He was going to give a recital and the notices were up all over the town. Boulder City rarely had such treats, and everyone was talking about the event.

" Are you coming ? " Ann asked Eileen. " I am going with my Mum and Dad."

" I—I don't think so. Does it cost a lot of money ? "

" Well, there are some seats in the gallery for sixpence."

" Sixpence ! Always sixpence," Eileen thought, and she wondered wistfully if she dared spend hers. She wanted terribly to hear someone really play the piano. She went home and took out her savings, counting them over thoughtfully. Most likely she could get some more the way she got this, but there was just the chance she would fail. No, the lessons mattered too much. With a heavy heart she put her coppers back. School would start in a week ; she dared not take the risk.

The day of the recital arrived. It was almost a gala day for the city. In those days so few famous people visited it that it was a real occasion. Those of Eileen's friends with whom she played had to leave her early in order to be washed and dressed in their best. The women folk dressed themselves up and the men hurried home to change.

Eileen could bear it no longer when she saw the cheerful parties making towards the hall. She ran to Mrs. Swift's, knocked and slipped in, shutting the door so quickly that it looked as if she were afraid of pursuit.

"Bless the child, what's the matter now?" Mrs. Swift could see that something was amiss.

"Nothing—— " Eileen sat down as far from the window as she could.

Like a wise woman Mrs. Swift took no further notice. She had come to know Eileen pretty well and knew that she was highly strung. Then suddenly a loud sob moved her to action.

"Now, child, what is it? I've never seen you cry before."

"Nothing." Eileen struggled to choke back the tears, but they would not be stopped. It was a kind of reaction. Having to wait for the lessons, and now not being able to go to the concert—well, she quite unexpectedly felt very sorry for herself. She longed forlornly for Daniel. He would have understood. Somehow he would have taken her.

"Eileen!" Mrs. Swift spoke sharply.

"Yes?" gulped Eileen.

"Tell me at once what is the matter." More gulps. "Now, blow your nose. It will make you feel better, and now tell me all about it." Mrs. Swift handed Eileen a handkerchief, and from the depths of it she gathered the sad tragedy.

"Everyone is going. I—I wanted to—but I can't. It—it costs too much."

"Going where?"

" To the—concert." This brought forth a fresh burst of tears.

" Well, you won't be able to go with a face like that ! " Mrs. Swift's words caused a shocked silence, followed by a big hiccough.

" There now, see what you have done. You won't be able to listen if you make that noise, will you ? Besides, they would turn you out."

" Listen—do you—do you mean——" but words failed Eileen.

" I mean you are a very silly little girl. Why did you not tell me before that you wanted to go ? Here is a shilling. Now, wash your face and hurry along."

" Oh, thank you, thank you ! " Mrs. Swift found a pair of almost suffocating arms round her neck and a very wet face pressed to hers.

" There, child, get on with it." She pushed Eileen gently away and blew her own nose very loudly.

Eileen was soon on her way and reached the hall just as the last few were crowding in.

" Sorry, young 'un. No children without an adult," the man at the box-office told her as she offered her shilling.

Unable to believe her ears, yet determined to get in, Eileen stood her ground.

" But I won't make a noise."

" Sorry, those are my orders."

" But I *will* go in ! " Eileen's temper began to rise.

" Take that child away," the man said briefly to one of the ushers. This was too much for Eileen. She was just about to brace herself for a struggle when she heard a cheery voice behind her.

" Hullo, Eileen, what's the trouble ? " It was her friend Dick and he was just about to take a ticket.

" They won't let me in." There was despair in Eileen's voice.

" Won't let you in ? That's nonsense. Give this young lady a ticket. She is coming in with me." He took Eileen's shilling without more ado and handed it through the window. " Come on," he said, and a very triumphant Eileen followed closely on his heels.

All her life Eileen never forgot that first recital. She was carried away to realms of which she had never dreamed ; she did not know that there was such music. Then and there she decided that one day she would play like that, that her hands would fly up and down the keyboard in just such a manner.

So vividly did she describe the recital to Mrs. Swift that the old lady almost fancied that she had heard it herself.

" It's a pity some folk have all the money," she muttered, as she watched Eileen skipping off happily down the garden path. Rather laboriously she went to the dresser drawer, and from the back of it extracted an old black leather bag. Breathing heavily, she sat down and poured some money out of the bag on to the table. Very carefully she began to count, examining every coin. Then, putting them all back, she found a piece of paper, and with great difficulty, wrote something. This she placed in the bag with the money and returned all to the drawer. With a sigh of satisfaction, she then made a cup of tea.

At last the day arrived for school to begin. Her friends thought Eileen quite demented when she joined them all smiles and eager to get there.

" It's beastly the holidays are over," Ann groaned.

" I'm glad," declared Eileen; but she would not say why, and she was on tenterhooks watching the clock for break. But, wonder of wonders, a message came from Sister Augustine and, breathless with excitement, Eileen ran to obey it. It was better than she hoped.

" You can have your first lesson now," Sister Augustine smiled encouragingly.

" Now ! " Eileen could hardly believe her ears.

" Sit down," and with those magic words life completely changed for Eileen. A piano was before her, there was someone to teach her all about it. With an extraordinary tenacity and a will to master everything she was shown, Eileen took with both hands the opportunity that was now hers. Sister Augustine was amazed from the first at the child's aversion to making a mistake. As a rule it was her fate to teach pupils who were only too eager to get the lessons over, hoping mistakes would not be noticed. Not so Eileen. She would check herself at once, and not only that—she would go over the passage again and again until she felt she had mastered it.

" She really is the most extraordinary child," Sister Augustine remarked to Sister Veronica after Eileen had had a number of lessons.

" I am finding her very inattentive this term. The child seems to dream. Perhaps the music lessons should be stopped."

" No, no ; don't do that. I am not at all sure, Sister Veronica, that she is not a child of very rare talent. Give me a little time, I shall soon know. In the meantime, be patient with her."

" Very well, but I think it very unlikely " ; and Sister Veronica went off to take her class. It was mathematics, and she tried very hard to be patient with Eileen ; but when, instead of nice neat sums, she found drawings of the bass and treble clef in Eileen's margin, she really was hard put to it to keep her word to Sister Augustine. The astonished Eileen went home wondering why she had been let off so lightly.

CHAPTER VIII

A Lot of Things Happen

IT was her uncle who first noticed the change in Eileen; not so much the change in herself as in her playing. Soon after she had started lessons Eileen had appeared again at the hotel.

" Please, can I play the piano ? "

" Yes, if you don't play too loudly. It's got few enough notes as it is." He let his niece in and shut his ears to what followed. It was the first of many requests from Eileen; in fact, it seemed that whenever the place was empty and she was not at school, she would slip in without a word and play, very softly. The piano had really become too bad to play upon, and it had been pushed into a small ante-room since Eileen's first visit. Her uncle found it quite easy not to be worried by the child's strumming, as he called it. Then one day as he was wiping up some glasses he became aware that it was not strumming, but that his niece was playing a very simple tune in an extremely efficient manner. He stole towards the ante-room and stood looking through the door, and was surprised by the look of concentration with which she was practising. Eileen was quite unaware of him. The melody came to an end, and she looked up. For a moment they regarded each other in silence. Her uncle was the first to break it.

" When did you learn to play like that ? "

Eileen flushed. She had not told anyone at home that she was having lessons.

" Oh, I just learnt." She tried to sound off-hand.

" So you just—learnt ! Very well, we will leave it at that ; play that thing again," and he walked to the window and listened very carefully.

" I think—I think I had better go." Eileen got up hurriedly when she had finished.

" Coming back to-morrow ? "

" Yes."

" You really are being taught, aren't you ? "

For a moment Eileen hesitated, then she decided to make a clean breast of the whole affair.

" You see, Mummie and Daddy couldn't afford the lessons, so I got the money myself," and she told him rather breathlessly how it had come about. " The trouble is, I shall have to get another sixpence for next term, and—and I'm so afraid they'll think it waste of money and stop me."

" Well, I must say ! " he exclaimed ; then suddenly began to laugh, at which Eileen looked a little hurt. " It's all right, kid. I'm not laughing at you. I like your spirit. You have good pioneer blood in you and it's showing itself. You get on with it and good luck to you."

" Oh, thank you, Uncle. I was so afraid you would

tell." Much relieved, Eileen started to leave, but as
she reached the door her uncle called after her.

"And don't you worry about that next sixpence.
I'll give it to you." He was a little overwhelmed by
the joy this caused and the thanks that followed. It
was some time later before he next saw Mr. Joyce and
then he acted on a decision to which he had given
much thought. What he said to his brother caused
the latter a great deal of surprise. So much so that
on his way home Mr. Joyce went to the school and
asked to see the music teacher.

Sister Augustine received him with interest. She
confirmed all that his brother had discovered on his
own.

"Yes, Mr. Joyce. It is my impression that your
child is a natural pianist; she has astounded me by
the progress she has made. I hope you will do all you
can to encourage her. I was not aware that you did
not know she was having lessons. Of course, if
Eileen does turn out to be outstanding, would you be
able to do anything about a musical career for
her?"

"No—I am afraid it is quite out of the question."
Rather reluctantly Mr. Joyce explained his difficulties,
and as he was leaving he made a request.

"I would be grateful to you if you would not
mention to Eileen that I have been to see you. I
have my own reasons."

Faintly puzzled, Sister Augustine agreed. "There
is no need to say anything."

That night, after Eileen had gone to bed, Mr. Joyce talked things over with his wife.

" Mind you, I don't know that I quite believe it. More than likely it's all a flash in the pan. The child will get tired of practising and that will be that."

" Fancy doing all that on her own." Mrs. Joyce was pleased with her daughter's achievement.

" That's what I am coming to. It's the kid's birthday soon and I think she ought to be given some encouragement," and he told his wife what he and his brother had in mind. Mrs. Joyce was so excited at the prospect that she could hardly wait for the day to arrive.

On the morning of her birthday Eileen woke up and pinched herself just to see if she felt any different for being ten years old. She decided she didn't, and got out of bed. Breakfast was a hurried meal, but they all wished her a happy birthday, and her mother gave her a new frock she had made. It was a lovely surprise, and was made out of a bit of red material Mrs. Swift had given her. It suited Eileen. John pressed a few sticky toffees into her hand, and her father gave her a penny to spend. This rather upset Eileen, and she wondered about it on her way to school. As a rule he always made her something special himself, like the beads she had had in Tasmania.

After school Eileen hurried down to the hotel, but her uncle was out. She went through into the ante-room, then stopped abruptly. There was no piano.

Quite suddenly the whole day was spoilt; she just could not believe it. What would she do? How could she learn if she couldn't practise?

"Uncle! Uncle!" she shouted, but only the barman answered from the back room.

A very dejected "birthday queen" returned home very slowly. Her mother had promised her something extra nice for her supper, but she did not feel hungry any more. She turned in at the gate, and to her surprise saw her father and uncle standing near the door.

"Where did you get to?" her father asked.

"I went down to see uncle."

At this the two men exchanged glances.

"Well, come on in; supper's ready."

Trying to look pleased, Eileen entered. The next moment she rushed forward, for there, in a corner of the room, was the piano.

"Oh!" she gasped. "Oh!"

"It's for you," her father said reassuringly at her look of wonderment.

"For my very own?"

"For your very own from us both; and what about giving us a tune?" Mr. Joyce opened the lid, and Eileen saw at once that the notes had been patched up.

"It's mended!" she exclaimed.

"And tuned!" laughed her father.

It was a very happy evening, and a birthday that Eileen always remembered. Her mother seemed as excited as she was, and they all seemed to take quite seriously the fact that she should play the piano. This time she did not mind when the holidays came, for she could practise as often as she liked—that is, unless her mother drove her from the house.

" Eileen, you must take Twink out," or " Eileen, do go and play like other children." The days were very full now, the happiest she had known for a long time. Two terms had passed, and Sister Augustine announced that an examiner would soon be out from England and she could enter for her Preliminary Musical Examination.

" But I think I could manage the Intermediate," argued Eileen. She knew that Doreen Smithers, who was much older, was working for that object, and she had seen the book she was using.

" No, Eileen. It's no good running before you can walk. An examination is not quite so easy as playing to me."

Eileen, however, had other ideas. The music, of course, was the difficulty : she could not afford to buy a book of her own. One day she plucked up her courage and waylaid Doreen as she came out of school.

" Please, Doreen, could you lend me your book for the Intermediate when you are not using it ? "

" Whatever for ? Oh, yes. You are Sister Augustine's wonder child ! " Doreen looked at Eileen with interest. Word had got about the school that they had a budding genius in their midst. Doreen had heard her play once, and recollected that it had surprised her that a lower form child could play so well. " Can't you get a copy of your own ? "

" No. You see, it's rather expensive."

" Oh, that's the trouble, is it ? All right, I haven't got a lesson for a week and I'm fed up with it. Give it me back on Monday."

" But your practising ? "

" My dear child, who wants to practise ? "

Eileen made the most of that week, and after that Doreen got sick of the sight of " the wonder child " as she called her, always hanging about for her copy when she had done with it.

" I'm not sure it wouldn't pay me better to buy you a copy," she teased one day, but somehow she had come to like the child and felt quite worried when for three whole days Eileen failed to collect the book.

" What happened ? " she asked, when she finally turned up.

" I had a cold."

" Then you'd better keep it for a few days to make up for lost time."

" May I really ? "

" Yes, of course. It's not so very long now. Does Sister Augustine think you will pass ? "

" I don't know." Eileen passed this off very hurriedly. " You see, I am a bit stuck over one part."

" Show me ! "

" It's here." Eileen quickly turned to the page.

" Yes, it's a bit tricky. I know, come home with me and perhaps I can help you."

With someone else to show her, Eileen soon overcame the difficulty, and she felt that Doreen was one of the kindest people she had ever met.

It was a week later that Sister Augustine told Eileen that she was definitely entering her for the Preliminary.

" But I think I can pass the Intermediate." A little doggedly Eileen repeated it this time.

" Now, Eileen, you have not worked on it, and even if you had, I am certain you would not be up to standard yet."

" Please, Sister Augustine, will you try me ? " Eileen looked at her in such a beseeching way that Sister Augustine felt that there was something behind it.

" Very well, see what you make of this." A little annoyed by her pupil's insistence and the fear that Eileen was getting a swollen head from her capacity to learn, she put the book in front of her. Needless to say, Eileen played it through almost to perfection.

" Oh, Eileen, what shall I do with you ? " Quite taken aback, Sister Augustine could not help laughing.

" May I ? "

" I suppose you knew I would say ' yes ' before you began."

" I hoped you would."

" Very well. We must work hard. Come to me to-morrow."

H

Eileen went and told Doreen of her triumph.

"I must say you are a dark horse." Doreen sounded highly amused. "It never entered my head you had not been told to work for it."

"That child absorbs music as blotting paper does ink," Sister Augustine told Sister Veronica some time later. "If she passes this exam something will have to be done about her."

Eileen did pass the exam, with Honours. It was some time before the results were known, but the examiner cross-questioned her teacher with such great interest afterwards that she knew it was a foregone conclusion.

"She is quite outstanding," he said. "A pity she should be buried here."

The words stayed in Sister Augustine's mind for a very long time. They worried her quite a lot, so that when the results were made known she spoke of her to the priest.

"I feel that we should do something about the child," she said.

"But what can we do? The family is very poor."

"Perhaps we could write to the Loreto Convent at Perth and put the case before them?" Sister Augustine suggested this a little against her inclination, for secretly the teaching of Eileen had become a great joy to her. A genuine musician herself, she rarely had such a pupil to deal with.

"Very well, Sister; if you think this child merits it, you shall have your own way."

"Thank you, Father," and Sister Augustine went back to her teaching while the priest wrote to Perth. He explained that they had an out-of-the-ordinary little girl with a great talent attending the day school who just lived for music; that according to the examiner, she showed outstanding ability, and that though only ten had just taken Honours in the Intermediate. He explained all the circumstances, sealed up the letter and posted it.

Within a week the answer came back. The Mother House of Loreto were quite prepared to take the child at their school in Perth and try to give her the advantages of which she sounded worthy, provided, of course, they had the full agreement of the parents and that money could be raised for her journey.

Meanwhile, Eileen, oblivious of all that was taking place on her behalf, was feeling very sad. Mrs. Swift, her greatest friend in Boulder City, had been found dead. It was a bitter blow for Eileen, and for some days she wandered about with hardly the heart to practise.

"She has had a long life, Eileen; you must not be too sad," said Mrs. Joyce. It was soon after this that her mother was asked to go to the Convent.

"Now, what have you been up to?" She eyed her daughter anxiously.

"Nothing." Eileen sounded a little uneasy, for she remembered the frogs she had put in Sister Veronica's desk. She waited anxiously until her mother returned, Mr. Joyce with her, as they had met on the way home. They both looked very serious, and Eileen's heart sank. Perhaps they had found out that it was she who had put the frogs in the desk. It had upset the class for the whole morning, for Sister Veronica, unknown to Eileen, was terrified of frogs and had promptly fainted.

"Well, Eileen, it seems that things have got a bit beyond us."

"Yes, Father." Eileen was still thinking of frogs.

"I won't hear of it," Mrs. Joyce put in.

"We've got to think of what is best for the child, Alice. Let her speak."

Eileen looked from one to the other, and her father held out his hand. They were not angry then; it was something else.

"They want us to let you go to school at Perth, Eileen. At their Convent there so that you can have a greater chance to become a musician. It happens they have a very fine teacher."

"To go right away from you?"

"Yes, Eileen, and it would be for a long time. I don't know how we are going to get the fare as it is."

"But I don't want to leave you all. I can go on learning here."

"No, you must get this clear: if you really want to become a pianist and learn everything that goes with it, you should go to a bigger school. It's a great opportunity, and young as you are, I want you to make up your own mind."

" The whole idea is absurd and you are not to think of it, Eileen." Her mother sounded dreadfully upset, and then and there Eileen decided she could not go away.

The next day, however, things were different. Eileen's school friends crowded round her. The news had slipped out. Some of them were very envious, others looked at her as though she were some rare specimen they had never seen before.

" Fancy them offering to have you at Perth ! " Gradually it dawned upon Eileen that here was a chance anyone would seize. Doreen's " So the wonder child has made it after all," impressed her even more ; but it was a talk with Sister Augustine that finally convinced her that she must accept such an opportunity.

" This afternoon we are going to have a small concert, and I want you to play. Your mother has promised to come. After she has heard you really play your best, I know she will want you to go."

" I do want to, really," Eileen explained. " It's just her ; she—will miss me."

Sister Augustine proved to be right. Sandwiched between the school songs, a halting violin solo, an uninspired duet and Doreen's really good piano solo, Eileen stood out with a strange brilliance for one so young. No longer could Mrs. Joyce deny that her daughter had a right to every chance that in her heart she had always craved for her.

" Other children go to boarding school, and it

won't be for long." That night her mother made light of her going, and Eileen began to feel excited, but her feelings were still mixed. To leave everyone she loved behind, to go quite alone to a big school— and then suddenly she remembered Twink! It was a bad moment, and all next day she was utterly miserable. It was her friend Ann who came to the rescue and got over that difficulty. She begged Eileen to lend him to her until she came back.

"Would you look after him? Would you really?"

"Yes, of course; I'll be awfully good to him, Eileen, and he does like me quite a lot."

"Yes, I know," and she brightened visibly; but the greatest difficulty of all was yet to be overcome— the matter of the journey money, not to mention clothes. But here the Joyces reckoned without the miners. Word had soon flashed round that Boulder City had an Infant Prodigy and then and there they got together. There was a good bit of gambling done for the next few nights, the winnings going towards the "Eileen fund".

"How kind everyone is," Mrs. Joyce said when they brought her the result.

Then to cap it all came Mrs. Swift's last thought. The authorities had been winding up her affairs and had found the old leather bag. Inside was £50, and a bit of paper bearing the words, in a very quavering hand, "For Eileen Joyce's music."

" Oh, Mummie, wasn't she good ! " Poor Eileen was almost in tears when she saw it, but soon the excitement of buying a real outfit of clothes wiped away all the sadness.

John teased his cousin for being so " dressed up ", and Eileen hardly recognized herself in a neat pinafore frock with a blue blouse. She did not like the hard leather shoes very much. They worried her feet and made them feel imprisoned. At the first opportunity she kicked them off.

The day arrived all too soon for her departure. It was a day fraught with emotion. Twink, interested in his new quarters, a large, airy stable, was not very aware of the sadness of his young mistress ; but there were the Sisters at the school, and John, who had become oddly silent, and her father, who dragged her from her mother's arms when, as the train was due to go, she clung to her and begged not to be sent away. So many good-byes ; and the train was very big, and going a long, long way. It was not to be wondered at that she was hardly aware of the flowers her school friends flung into the carriage window, or Doreen's last challenge of, " Make us proud of you, wonder child."

As the train began to move she sat very still and very white, wishing that never in her life had she seen a piano. She sat so still and tight in her corner that at last the passenger opposite could endure it no longer. She prodded Eileen suddenly with her umbrella and held out a large peach.

"Here, eat this," she ordered, and wondered what in the world people were thinking about to send such a forlorn child on such a long journey all by herself. By the end of the journey she had heard all about it, for they had become good friends.

CHAPTER IX

Quite a New Life

EILEEN, on her arrival at Perth, was at first quite unable to absorb her new surroundings. She had a hazy recollection of a kind-faced Sister who claimed her as she stood a little fearfully amidst the noise and bustle of the big station. There was the drive up to the Loreto Convent, "Osborne," which lay seven miles out of the town. She remembered her pleasure at the first sight of the Swan River, with its deep blue waters ; and as they approached the school she had caught a glimpse of a large expanse of ocean. The school buildings looked big and imposing in comparison with those to which she had been used. She just could not take it all in. Five hundred miles had been a long journey, with the added anxiety of being alone and only in charge of the guard. There had been the fear that he might forget her. True, the lady in the opposite corner had been very kind, but she was not her mother.

" I think I should put that child to bed for a day or two," the Mother Superior had advised kindly, after she had seen Eileen. Then had come the awful moment when the clanging of the bell had brought hundreds of girls flocking to the lovely grounds as

Eileen nervously followed a Sister across to one of the separate houses where she was to sleep. Eileen was not aware that she looked rather a caricature in her ill-fitting clothes, with an unaccustomed hat perched on the top of her unruly locks, but she was acutely conscious of the way in which some of the girls stared at her, some amused, some friendly, and others purely challenging.

"Golly! Have you seen the new girl?" Nora Haddon asked her special chum, Sadie, after she had watched Eileen disappear into her quarters.

"No, what is she like? How old?"

"About our age, rather small, but her clothes! You never saw anything so funny!" With the quick eye of children, they discussed Eileen's manifest shortcomings.

"Well, perhaps she comes from the backwoods, but she may be good at games," Sadie said hopefully. She was captain of the net-ball team.

"Only time will show! We can soon test her," Nora agreed.

Time did show. They were difficult, but not entirely unhappy days that followed for Eileen. Everything was so new, utterly different from anything she had known before. Wherever she turned there were rules. Rules that stopped her running into the open when she wanted to. Bells to get up to, bells to go to bed by. Chapel every day, meals always at the same hours, the constant check on her behaviour.

" Eileen, sit up ! "

" Eileen, take your elbows off the table and don't hold your knife like that."

" Eileen, the floor is not the place for your things ! "

" Eileen, look at your hair ! Go and comb it."

" Eileen, you are not to run along the corridors."

She was never, never being able to go away by herself; there were classes for mending; there were letters to parents that had to be written on a certain day whether one felt like it or not. She wrote to Daniel and told him all her troubles, and he wrote back cheering her up and telling her how glad he was that she really wanted to play the piano.

Then came the first day she had to play net-ball. She hated it from the first moment. The ball bounced in her face and hit her hands ; she seemed to get in the way of everyone she should have helped, and threw the ball, if she did catch it, to those wearing red bands instead of green. Poor Eileen, she had never played a team game before and it left her quite bewildered.

" Of all the stupid little muffs ! " Nora said unkindly.

" I'm not a muff ! " Eileen flared up, not being at all sure what a " muff " was.

" Yes, you are. You didn't even try to catch the ball half the time."

" Well, I didn't want to. It's a silly game and— and I don't want to be on your side and I won't play ! "

"Oh!" groaned Sadie; "you are one of those stupid little won't-playites, are you? Very well, you've asked for it and you are going to get it. You will have to play because it's the rule, and we shall jolly well see that you do play, so there." In fury Sadie led away the little group who had gathered to hear this dressing down.

Eileen stared after them, hating them all. She wondered what to do next. They were all going down to bathe and she did not particularly want to go with them, but she knew she had to.

"I hate games, too." Eileen turned and saw a tall, thin, red-headed girl whom she had noticed once or twice, but had never spoken to.

"Do you?" Eileen looked interested.

"Yes, but I never said so. You were rather silly to." They started to walk together across the grounds.

"I don't see what they are making such a fuss about."

"Oh, some of them are games mad. You've got to do your bit for the team and all that, otherwise they just don't know you exist."

"I think it is all stupid. Where do we bathe?"

"In the Swan River. You'll like that. Do you swim?"

"Yes. Oh! isn't this lovely?" Eileen paused as, having crossed the grounds by a zigzag path, they reached some steps. Far below lay the Swan River in all its beauty. The deep-sea blue of its waters looked more than inviting. The lovely green foliage of its banks cast beautiful shadows. Here and there was a slant of white as little boats darted busily about.

" Come on, there are three hundred and forty-nine steps to go down before we can get in it," said Priscilla.

They started to clamber down; the others were more than half-way.

" Are there any black swans ? " Eileen asked. Daniel had told her about them.

" Yes, you see them sometimes. When we have picnics they come up for scraps. Where do you come from ? "

" Tasmania." And as they went down Eileen told her new friend a little of how she had come to the school.

" That's rather funny, because I am dotty about the violin. Perhaps we'll meet in the music rooms sometime."

" Do lets," Eileen agreed eagerly, " but I've had no lessons yet. I can't think why."

" Perhaps Sister John has not been able to fit you in. It was nearly half-term before you came."

" I hope I won't have to wait until next term then." Eileen sounded really anxious.

" I don't expect so. Come on, here we are. You go in that hut. I have to go over there because I am in a higher form than you," and Priscilla ran off.

The Junior School were already in the water, splashing around and laughing merrily. They had, for the school's own private use, a small jetty, and the part where they could bathe was enclosed. Eileen was very excited at the thought of being in the water once again. She shed her clothes quickly and slipped into her new neat swim suit, then, as was her custom, she stepped out and took a flying dive into the water. She was quite oblivious to the fact that she was breaking one of the strictest rules. Forms always had to go into the water together so that the mistress in charge could count each girl.

The water was cold and clear. Eileen surfaced and struck out happily, feeling a gorgeous sense of freedom. Then suddenly she was aware of an angry voice close to her ear.

"Eileen, go on shore at once. Why must you always break the rules ? " It was one of the prefects, annoyed that she had had to swim after her.

"Why ? " she asked defiantly.

"Send that child in at once ! " Miss Burrow's voice thundered across the water, and Eileen was aware that most eyes were now turned in her direction.

"Selfish little pig! Now you've upset Miss Burrows and she'll have us in early." Sadie looked angrily towards Eileen as she spoke.

This was too much for Eileen's pent-up spirits. She turned in the water and before Sadie was aware of her intention, had dived under and grabbed her victim by the legs. She pulled her under and did not let go of the struggling, spluttering Sadie until she herself needed breath. Before Sadie had recovered herself she had struck out strongly to the shore with half the by now infuriated juniors after her. To duck their Captain! Had Eileen realized it, it was the worst possible thing she could have done, but for the moment she was in the clutches of the angered Miss Burrows.

"Eileen, where are your senses? How dare you go into the water without coming to me first? I cannot think what you were thinking of. You seem quite incapable of keeping rules. I shall have to report you to the Mother Superior."

"Yes, Miss Burrows."

"Why did you do it?"

But Eileen was too miserable to answer. She was beginning to be aware that the carefree, gypsy life she had led ill-prepared her for the rules of the school.

Tea was a wretched affair. Nobody spoke to her. Affronted by the treatment of their Captain, the Juniors had sent her to Coventry. She was left out of everything and nobody took any notice of her, a treatment that she utterly failed to understand. To crown it all was the interview with Mother Thomas, who at first seemed to take a serious view of the wilful breach of the rules. But Mother Thomas understood children, and seeing that Eileen was really distressed, she probed a little deeper.

"Now, Eileen, there must be some explanation." At the first show of kindness, Eileen gave way.

"There—there are so many rules. I—I can't seem

to remember them all, and I had not heard about this one."

"Oh, I see," Mother Thomas understood now. "Very well, Eileen, I shall not punish you for this, but remember that now you are with many others you have to make it your business to know and keep the rules. Now run along."

"Yes, Mother."

"Oh, I was forgetting. Sister John wished to see you at five-thirty." She was quite startled by the transformation that came over Eileen. From utter dejection she became alive and interested.

"What a queer little person," she thought, as Eileen hurried away.

"Hullo!" said Priscilla, who had been waiting for her.

"You had better not talk to me. The others won't."

"I don't care what the others do." Priscilla slipped a friendly arm through Eileen's.

"I've got to see Sister John at five-thirty." Eileen was bursting with information.

"I expect you are going to start lessons."

"Oh, if only I were, I wouldn't care about anything. If only I could begin!"

"That's the spirit! Come and tell me what happens." They parted at the music-room door, and Eileen went in happily.

"So you are Eileen Joyce." Sister John looked at her new pupil in surprise. She seemed so small to be as far advanced in her music as the report had said.

" Yes, Sister," Eileen answered a little shyly ; then her eyes wandered to the piano and lighted up. Sister John was quick to note this.

" Sit down and play me something. Anything you like. Try to forget I am here." Sister John soon realized that her last remark was quite superfluous, for in a moment Eileen had forgotten her very existence. Like a child who had been hungry for too long, she put into her playing all that had been pent-up in her, all the newness and strangeness of everything, all the homesickness mingled with the joy of touching the piano again. The last notes died away, and for a moment Sister John regarded Eileen in silence. She

I

was fully aware that the child was still far away, not conscious of her surroundings.

"Eileen!" she said very softly.

"Yes?" Like a sleep-walker who had been gently awakened, Eileen became aware of her teacher.

"You have a very great talent. You and I are going to work very hard together."

"Yes, Sister."

There was complete understanding between them now. The teacher realized that here was a great future pianist. There was no need to pretend about it. The pupil, for her part, recognized sympathy and understanding and felt in complete harmony.

"These are the times of your lessons and you may practise in number four whenever you are free." Sister John did not realize when she said this the slight complication which would arise later, for Eileen's practising soon became a feature to music lovers who would leave their own practising rooms, drawn by the power of her playing.

"Oh, may I really?" Again that quick, friendly smile flashed across Eileen's face. All her troubles were over now. She could get at the piano whenever she liked. It was just too good to be true.

It was a very transformed Eileen who joined Priscilla some time later; so transformed that the Juniors felt that their "Coventry" was falling somewhat flat, and were a little shaken in consequence. So much so that they collared Priscilla and pitched into her for talking to Eileen.

" It's not fair," Nora complained.

" I think you are all rotten ! " Priscilla answered back. " That kid comes from miles away. She has lived in the bush and isn't used to our ways, yet you pick on her as if she had done something really wrong. You haven't given her a chance since she came. But you wait, all of you. I bet she is going to give you the surprise of your lives."

" Surprise, my foot ! " snorted Sadie, but their indignation quickly faded away before Priscilla's outburst.

Shortly after that Eileen's form found a new subject for their attention. The term was drawing to an end, and the all-prevailing interest of the whole school was the Swimming Sports. Heats were being swum off for the final of the hundred yards, and there was also the selection of the teams for the Junior and Senior Swimming Trophies. Eileen had been forced to play games, but she found that most of the team ignored her and passed her over. Sadie had decided that she was a dud and that was that. In the water they ignored her also, so she amused herself as far away from them as possible, playing around with Priscilla.

It was one particularly hot Saturday about three weeks after her ducking of Sadie that Joan Summers, the swimming Captain, had wandered down to watch the Juniors. Eileen was blissfully unaware of why the others were swimming as fast as they knew how, hoping that Joan might select them. With Priscilla, she was diving, then racing her back to the jetty.

" Who is that kid ? " Joan pointed towards her.

" That ? Oh, that's the new kid, Eileen Joyce. Frightful little creature," answered Nora, who happened to be near.

" She may be frightful, but how she can move ! " Thoroughly interested, Joan walked along the jetty and waited for Eileen and Priscilla to return.

" Suppose you two swim across for me as far as you can," she suggested as they reached her.

" All right," agreed Priscilla ; " come on, Eileen ;" but Eileen hung back ; she suspected more trouble. "Eileen, that's the swimming Captain. Don't be a goof ! " Priscilla hissed. " Come on, you can't beat me."

" Can't I ! " Eileen took up the challenge, and in a second they were racing neck and neck, but Eileen managed to outstrip her friend in the last few yards.

" Come on, we'd better go back to Joan ; she is waving." Leisurely they returned and scrambled out beside the Captain.

" You have plenty of speed ! " Joan looked at Eileen approvingly. " I shall put you down for the Junior Trophy."

" Oh, Eileen, how splendid ! " Priscilla looked as pleased as if it were she.

" But, please, I'd rather not. You see, I haven't much time to spare."

" Don't talk nonsense. Of course you've time, and you've jolly well got to swim for the school." Joan turned away without more ado.

Eileen turned angrily upon her friend. " But I don't want to swim for the school."

" Now look here, Eileen, I've stuck by you and got myself pretty unpopular for doing so. After all, I am older than you and you have jolly well got to listen to me. Here is something you can do really well, and it's up to us all to give the school something. I shall take a very poor view if you won't do this."

" Oh ! " exclaimed Eileen. " Do you really think I should ? "

" Of course I do. After all, this is a jolly fine school, and unless you are going to take part in the life of it you will soon find that nobody has any time for you."

" But my music ? "

" That's a sort of personal thing, isn't it ? Well, this isn't. I know I sound beastly like the Head, but it will do you good to do something for others."

" Yes—yes, I think I see what you mean. All right, I'll swim."

" Good for you."

Well pleased, Priscilla realized that she had won her case, and it was with some amusement that she watched the sensation when Eileen's name appeared as one of the contestants for the Swimming Trophy.

" Wonders will never cease ! " exclaimed Sadie.

" I expect she'll make a mess of it," grunted Nora.

But Eileen did not make a mess of it. She defeated both Nora and others of her form with an amazing ease in the heats that followed. Only against Sadie did she have a really breathless finish, at which members of her form shouted and cheered, even calling her name. Somewhat surprised, her form realized that she stood as their sole representative against the other forms, and the astonished Eileen found herself the centre of attraction during the following week. She became quite popular, and even when she spent most of her free time practising instead of playing with the others, she found their remarks about it had become quite good-natured.

The day of the sports arrived at last. It was a whole holiday. Parents arrived; everyone was laughing and happy.

"Look at all those people!" Slightly startled, Eileen regarded the audience who thronged the edge of the pool.

"You don't want to take any notice of them." Priscilla propelled her to the bathing huts, where excited members of her form thronged around her, wishing her luck.

The Senior Trophy was swum first, and a popular win was made by Joan for the Fifth Form. Then the entrants for the Junior Trophy lined up at the starting-point, six of them, all determined to be the winner. Eileen's friends were slightly nervous. They knew her habit of being a trifle slow to get off the mark, her fatal aptitude to dream. There was a tense silence as the starter prepared them; then came the start, and cheers broke out. There was a slight groan as Eileen was the last to dive, and for a time did not seem to be making up the loss.

" Come on, Jean ! "

" Keep it up, Olive."

" Ma—bel ! "

" Eileen—Eileen, make it up !"

Rival shouts urged on the swimmers, and suddenly fresh cheers broke out as Eileen put on a spurt, and with grace and a clean stroke, she cut through the water with surprising speed. She fought Mabel for the first place as the tape was almost reached. For a second it looked as if she wouldn't make it ; then a great roar went up, as by about a head, she wrested the Trophy from a higher form. And so it was that Eileen's first term ended more happily than it had begun. She had proved her worth to her form mates, and was accepted as one of them at last.

CHAPTER X

Wonders Never Cease !

THE terms that followed were happy ones for Eileen, made happy by the fact that the doubt which had been in her mind about holidays was removed once and for all. When the school broke up she was sent home just as the others were, to run wild with Twink, to visit her uncle, to play with John or help her mother. It was all too good to be true. In the evenings they would sometimes have a sing-song, or Eileen would play to them. Life was good, and she returned to school each time with new zeal and a thirst for all Sister John could teach her.

Soon it was Christmas term, and the thought of presents to be made, and of the school concert looming horribly near, caused the Juniors quite a headache.

"What's that you are making?" Sadie perched herself on the edge of Eileen's desk and fingered some bits of felt.

"I'm trying to make a pair of felt slippers for my mother. Miss Jones showed me how, but they look a queer shape!"

"They certainly do," laughed Sadie. "Priscilla, look at Eileen's slippers. Whoever wears them will have to walk backwards!"

" They won't."   Eileen looked up and grinned at Priscilla who had just joined them.

" Yes, they will.   You are sewing the toe on to the heel."

" Oh, dear, so I am !   It's quite hopeless ; I never do seem any good at this sort of thing."

" No, it isn't.   Here, give it to me ; I'll start it for you."   Good-naturedly, Sadie seized the shoe, and Eileen sat back with a sigh of relief.

" It's no good you going into one of your dreams ; I want your full attention.   Look at me, now ! " Priscilla planted herself firmly in front of Eileen. She knew it was the only way of getting her to listen.

" What is it ? "

" This wretched concert for the blind.   Stella has gone sick and cannot sing.   Will you ask Sister John if you could play something ? "

" Yes, that's a good idea," Sadie put in.   " It's about time we heard what the dear child can do." Sadie copied their form mistress so well that they all laughed.   " We can easily put a comedy turn on afterwards to cheer ourselves and the audience up ! "

" I'll give you comic ! "   Eileen seized a piece of felt and threw it at Sadie.   " But honestly, I expect it would rile the Seniors if we put on a straight piano solo in our part, because Alice is playing one in theirs."

" Alice ! "   There was scorn in Priscilla's voice. " The ' Merry Peasant ' is about her mark.   You can do much better than that."

"Put her down," Sadie interposed firmly. "She'l
fill up time, anyway."

"I had better ask Sister John." Eileen saw there
was little chance of escape. She had, however, a feeling of hope that her teacher would not permit it, bu
Sister John was pleased with the idea.

"Since they have asked you, dear, I think it is a
good opportunity. You will have to get used to playing in public if you are going to make a career of it."

"Not much hope of that!"

"We shall see. Your progress has pleased me more
than I can say. Now, what are you going to play?
What about something of Grieg's?"

"Yes. Oh dear, I know my hands will shake and
I'll forget every note."

"No, they won't, not once you start. You'll forget everything except your playing, that's half your
secret. You can have the book in front of you."

"No, I don't want the music."

"Very well, it's for you to decide."

"I feel all kind of bubbly inside already and the
concert's not for a week. What shall I feel like on
the day?"

"More bubbly still," laughed Sister John, who
thoroughly understood this pupil of hers. She didn'
add that she was also feeling "bubbly". She knew
now without a shadow of doubt that Eileen stood
quite in a class of her own, and although she had not
wanted to thrust her talent upon the school, she had
begun to wish for an opportunity. She most ardently

wanted her own opinion of the child to be confirmed by others.

On the day of the concert, Sister John joined the others in the big hall and watched the visitors crowding in. The stage was prettily decorated, and the prefects were showing people to their seats. There was an air of excitement and festivity, for even those not interested in the concert were looking forward to the huge tea afterwards. At last the Mother Superior took her place, the lights were lowered, there were a few last-minute whispers. The curtain went up and the choir sang the school song.

Item followed item. A Junior breathlessly recited a piece of poetry, and the Seniors did their sketch. Priscilla played a violin solo with marked talent, winning much applause. The comic turn became funnier than was intended, since stage fright stepped in and lines got mixed. Alice Trevor sang " Goodbye for Ever," and failed on the top note because she could feel the school take a breath and wait for it, just as they always did when she practised. She came off the stage thirsting for their blood, and declaring to Eileen, whose turn it was next, that " they were a rotten audience."

" Well, nobody wanted you to sing," Priscilla answered truthfully, afraid that it would upset Eileen. Nobody liked Alice very much. She always would push herself forward.

" Now then, Eileen, show them ! " Priscilla gave her a slight push, and the next minute, for the first time in her life, Eileen was alone on a platform and was fully aware of the countless eyes upon her. At that moment she wished she could sink through the floor and never be heard of again. Somehow she reached the stool and sat down, and at once the nearness of the keys reassured her. She stared at them very hard, and an excited "She's forgotten her piece" from the wings failed to ruffle her. Then, just as the audience was beginning to think that something was amiss, Eileen began to play. The visitors listened at first with benevolent indulgence, while her school-fellows prepared for some minutes of boredom; but Sister John, watching, noticed the change come over them as with every second Eileen forgot she had an audience and the warmth of her playing increased.

"Who is that child?" somebody whispered, only to be "shushed" at once. Even the Juniors were sitting forward on their chairs, wondering why they were feeling electrified. The playing came to an end, and Eileen slipped off the stool. Sister John saw her jump visibly as a burst of applause broke forth, awakening her to the fact of the pleased faces before her and the ovation she had caused. A little at a loss as to what was expected of her, she turned hurriedly to escape.

"Bow, Eileen," Priscilla called from the wings; and turning, flushed with excitement at their reception, she bobbed quickly and almost ran from the stage.

"Go on again. You've made a hit." Priscilla

pushed her back as the applause continued, and this time Eileen made a pretty little curtsy in the middle of the stage.

The curtain was lowered and an excited buzz of conversation broke out. Everyone wanted to know who Eileen was. Parents heaped questions upon their daughters, and the Juniors assumed an air of importance because the " Sensation " belonged to them.

" Well, wonders do never cease," said the surprised Nora to Sadie. " I suppose this accounts for her being not quite like us."

" I suppose it does," agreed Sadie, who knew that Nora had held out against Eileen until now. In fact, it had been the one thorn in her flesh.

" Come on, let's have some tea." Sadie returned to her parents and they entered the dining-room, where already Eileen seemed to be holding a small court. Priscilla was near her looking as pleased as Punch.

" I must say the kid isn't putting on side," Nora remarked, after watching her closely for a moment.

" I'd like a word with her," Sadie's mother said, and Eileen was called over.

" This is my mother, Eileen."

The greetings over, Mrs. Morgan asked Eileen several questions about her music. " Are you going to take it up professionally ? " she enquired.

" I want to, but you see, I don't think we can afford it," Eileen answered simply.

" I think, if that is the case, something must be done about it." Mrs. Morgan, who was very keen on music, recognized that here was talent that must not be ignored, and must be helped somehow.

Sister John was pleased to note in the days that followed that Eileen had taken her brief triumph all in her stride. It seemed to give her fresh incentive to work even harder, and she was loth to be away from the piano a minute longer than she need.

" Really, child, there is no need to work quite so hard ! You learn these studies before I have had time to find you more."

" But don't you see, this is the only chance I have. When I leave you it will be the end of my lessons." Eileen was astonished that Sister John had not grasped the importance of every minute to her.

" Is that what you are worrying about ? "

" Yes."

" Well, try not to. You see, Eileen, there are people in the world who really love music—who would do anything to advance it, and there is always a chance that someone like that might hear you play and make it possible for you to go on with your studies."

" Do you think so—do you really think so ? " The depression that had settled upon Eileen lifted abruptly. She got up and walked up and down the room, a habit she had when she was agitated or excited.

" Yes, I do think so. And I pray every day that it may come about. You must pray too."

" Oh, I do, really I do. You see, I want to be a great pianist, a really great one. I love it so much."

" Yes, I knew that the first time I heard you play. Always feel like that, child, and I know God will help you."

It happened that Sister John's faith was rewarded sooner than she had dared to hope. It was a habit of famous musicians when visiting Perth sometimes to call upon the nuns and give them a short recital ; and it so happened that Percy Grainger, the folk-lore pianist, being in that part of the country, decided to drop in and play for them. Sister John was on tenter-hooks all the time. She revelled in his playing, but was longing to seize the opportunity which she knew had been sent. As their thanks were being made she craved the Mother Superior's permission to speak with the musician about Eileen.

" Yes, if you really think the child merits it. Not that I can see it will help in any way."

" Thank you, Mother," and she followed her eagerly towards Mr. Grainger.

" Sister John is our chief music teacher here, Mr. Grainger. I think she has a request to make."

" I hope it is in my power to grant it." Percy Grainger bowed gravely.

" Your love for music makes me bold. We have a child here of very poor family, and unless I am mistaken she is a natural pianist of very rare talent. I wonder if, out of the goodness of your heart, you would allow her to play to you ? "

"Why—yes." There was a slight suggestion of doubt in Mr. Grainger's voice. So often had proud mothers or ambitious teachers voiced the same request, exposing him to ten minutes of polite but unenthusiastic listening.

"Thank you." Although Sister John recognized the doubt, she chose to act only on the acceptance "I will bring her to you."

In a few moments there was a hue and cry for Eileen, and she was retrieved from her hated game of net-ball and hurried to Sister John.

"Eileen, quickly wash your hands. I want you to come and play for someone."

"Yes, Sister John." Thankfully Eileen ran and did as she was told, but she did not bother with her unruly curls and appeared looking rather wild.

"This is the child. I am afraid I fetched her straight from a game of net-ball. Eileen, this is Mr. Grainger. He is very kindly going to hear you play."

"The composer of 'Shepherds Hey?'" Eileen whispered to Sister John excitedly.

"Now, suppose you play me something," said Mr. Grainger. He had taken immediately to the wild-looking child and liked the business-like way she settled down at the piano. As soon as she began to play he realized that here was no "young hopeful," but a child of extraordinary talent. He listened for a long time, urging her to play anything she knew. When at last she stopped, he took her hands in his, feeling them, noting their firmness, the already strongly developed finger-tips.

"I suppose you know this child should be sent to America to study?" he said to Sister John.

"To America? Then you think as I do?"

"My good Sister, there is no doubt whatever. Sometimes pianists are born and you have one of them here." He smiled down at Eileen, who was looking at him with excited, starry eyes.

"I am afraid America is out of the question. You see, there is no money behind Eileen. I just cannot see how we can give her that advantage."

"Never mind, Eileen." Percy Grainger noted the sudden dashed look in her eyes. "You keep on with your studies. You are in very good hands. In the meantime, I will see if anything can be done about the future."

When he had gone, Eileen flung her arms round Sister John.

"Do you think he will? Do you really think he will?" There were tears in her eyes and she was trembling with excitement.

"There, there, child, you mustn't get so strung

K

up over things. Now dry your eyes and go and find the others. I think, Eileen, our prayers have been answered.''

Not pausing to weigh the pros and cons, and quite certain that her prayers had been heard, Eileen rushed off to the Junior common-room. Flinging open the door she announced to one and all, '' I'm going to America ! ''

'' America ? ''

'' Whatever for ? ''

'' It's miles away ! ''

'' Who said so ? ''

A chorus of voices answered her as they gathered round.

'' Percy Grainger. He has just heard me play. He—he says I must go there to study.''

'' But, Eileen, how will you get there ? '' Sadie asked.

'' You said you hadn't got any money ! You need lots in America.'' Nora was practical at once.

'' Will your parents let you go ? '' Priscilla asked the question that brought Eileen down to earth with a bang.

'' Oh, I'd forgotten them.''

'' Well, soon enough when it happens,'' Sadie said wisely. '' Tell us all about it ''; and although slightly damped, Eileen told them all that had happened.

'' It seems the ' Sensation ' really is a sensation after all,'' Nora exclaimed, not unkindly this time.

" Will you give us all free seats when you are famous ? " someone else asked, and after that Eileen had to put up with a good deal of banter, but she did not mind. Once more her head was in the clouds.

True to his word, Percy Grainger tried to raise public interest upon Eileen's behalf. Before he went away he wrote to the newspapers, and amongst other things said, " She is the most transcendentally gifted child I have ever heard," and he suggested a fund should be raised to send her to America.

With this knowledge Eileen went home for the holidays, and told her parents of his visit and all that he had said.

" But, Eileen, there is no need to make a decision until we hear officially from the school," Mr. Joyce reasoned. " Besides, you talk about going to America as if it were walking to the other side of the street. Have you thought of all that it means ? "

" And the cost of it ? What if this appeal comes to nothing ? " Mrs. Joyce hated to damp her daughter's dreams, but it had been a big enough sacrifice to part with her for school. She felt that this wild idea, which as far as she could see had no hope of fulfilment, was putting them all to far too great a strain.

" If it was possible and I became famous, would you mind then ? " Eileen persisted.

" Fame isn't everything," her father commented. " We might not see you for years."

" Oh, I hadn't thought of that." This was the first remark to have any real effect, and after it, Eileen let the matter rest. She made the most of her time at home and sought out her old friends.

" So the wonder child becomes more and more wonderful ! " Doreen, who had left school and was now herself giving music lessons, paused when she met Eileen in the street.

" I shall never live that down, shall I ? " laughed Eileen.

" I couldn't help it. But I am so glad you are doing so well."

" Most likely I owe it all to you. If you had not lent me your book I would not have been sent to Perth."

" Who knows ? As a reward, you can come and play to me. What about tea to-morrow ? "

" I'd love to."

" And may I say ' how the child has grown ' ? " Doreen teased.

" Please don't. Everyone says it. I think they expect me never to be any different."

" Yes, it is a silly remark, isn't it ? " And Doreen went on her way.

The next day, after she had heard Eileen play, she hit on the idea of showing her off a little.

" Boulder City has jolly well got to know what has been flowering in their midst ! "

" But, Doreen, they won't want to."

" You leave it to me, my child. It will be a good

advertisement for me when I put over my name, ' Helped Eileen Joyce to pass the Intermediate '."

" You really are the limit ! "

" Limit or no limit, you are going to do as I say."

" Very well," Eileen agreed meekly, and some days later she played to a large gathering of miners and friends in Doreen's house, and everyone liked her natural modesty and manner of playing. They agreed amongst themselves that the money they had helped to collect in order to send her away had been well spent.

" It certainly seems the kid has worked," one of them said.

"Maybe there is something else we can do about it when the time comes," a friend of Mr. Joyce's suggested, and Eileen, eating her fill of the lovely tea Doreen's parents had provided, little realized she was a step nearer her goal.

CHAPTER XI

Wilhelm Backhaus Decides

THE summer term had been in full swing for some time and Eileen was lying lazily in the shade of a tree with a few cronies, watching a cricket match. By now she had given up all hope of hearing any more from Percy Grainger and had decided that he had quite forgotten her.

" He is a very busy man," Sister John had comforted. " He will not forget. He has written to the papers, but these things take time."

" I don't expect he even remembers that he has heard me play," Eileen answered bitterly.

" Now, Eileen, you are being unreasonable. After all, even if he could find a way for you to go to America, there would still be many obstacles to overcome. You must be patient."

But that was the one thing Eileen could not be when it was anything connected with her music. The knowledge that there would be a future for her if only she could afford to go abroad filled her with despair. She knew now that this was the only thing she wanted—to play her way through life ; to study and study, and to make up for lost time. She knew from the books she had read and the knowledge she had gained that the really great musicians had as a rule started their training at the age of seven or even younger. Time had begun to matter very much to her.

"Eileen, Reverend Mother wants you." A small junior delivered the message, then scurried away.

"Oh, golly! What have I done now?" Eileen sat up and brushed the grass off her tunic.

"I expect it's more a case of what you haven't done," Sadie teased. Eileen was always in trouble for forgetting things. "If you wouldn't sit and dream, Eileen, you could be quite brilliant," she said, imitating their form mistress.

"Well, well, you may never see me again!" Eileen struck a tragic air which made them all laugh, then hurried into the school building. Her steps flagged a bit as she neared the door, but she knocked boldly and entered.

"Daniel!" There was a glad cry and she was in his arms. "Daniel, where have you come from?" For a moment she forgot the Reverend Mother; then with horror, she recollected. Disentangling herself from Daniel's giant hug, she bobbed respectfully.

"It's all right, Eileen; it's good to see an old friend."

"Yes, Mother—it's—it's been a long time."

"He wants to take you out for the day, so hurry and get your things and meet him in the hall."

"Oh, thank you." With another bob and an excited glance at Daniel, she was off.

"I just can't believe it!" she exclaimed as they re-met in the hall.

"And I just can't believe you!" Daniel smiled as for a moment he looked her up and down. "You have grown out of all recognition—quite a young lady, in fact. How old are you now?"

"Twelve and a half."

"My, how times flies. What shall we do?"

"Let's go into Perth, and then will you take me to King's Park? I've always wanted to see it but never got there."

"The top of Mount Eliza, isn't it? You still love mountains?"

"Of course I do. You know, Daniel, when I first came here I could not bear all the rules and being shut in class. I used to sit and pretend that I had escaped and was running up your mountain to find you."

"And I bet you got no marks!"

They both laughed and soon were chatting away, trying to fill in the gaps of the past years. Daniel told her as they drove into Perth how he had stuck to his writing and was now making quite a comfortable income.

"I've left you two books to read when you get back."

"Oh, thank you. What fun!"

"You'll see that you have become the heroine of one of them, you and Twink."

"Really, Daniel? You know I'm worried about Twink. The girl who is looking after him for me is going away, and there is just a chance I might, too, and I don't know what will become of him. He is so sweet, he always remembers me.''

'' You'd better let me have him.''

'' Would you, Daniel ? I should hate to think of him just being left.''

'' Of course I will. But what's this about going away ? ''

'' Well, it's a long story and I don't really think it's going to happen.'' Eileen sounded suddenly miserable.

'' Tell me all about it over lunch.''

'' Yes, I will ;'' and when they were at last seated in a lovely restaurant with an orchestra playing in the distance and a view of the Swan River to delight their eyes, Eileen told him all her hopes and fears.

'' Well, if Percy Grainger really said that, Eileen, I don't think you need give up hope. Something will be done. And do you know what we are going to do before we go to King's Park ? ''

'' What ? ''

'' I am going to hire a practising room at one of the music shops, and you are going to give me a concert all to myself. I've never heard you play.''

'' I'd like that, Daniel. I'd like to play to you.''

'' Eat up, then, and let's go.''

Eileen enjoyed the hour that followed, as, in fact, she loved the whole day. Daniel's '' Yes, kid, you'll climb to the heights all right,'' after she had played, rewarded her more than anything else could have done. She began to feel again that it was possible, that somehow it would come about, this dream of hers.

In high spirits they ascended Mount Eliza and stood looking down upon the river, tranquil in its deep rich blue, fringed with little houses, their red roof-tops startling against the mass of olive foliage in which they nestled. The city of Perth looked clear cut and dazzling in its whiteness as the sun shone upon it.

"It's all so lovely," exclaimed Eileen. "Come on, let's explore!"

They set off into the great park, walking along the main drive bordered by its avenue of flowering gums, which excited Eileen with their wondrous array of colours.

"Look, Daniel, Kangaroo Paw!" Eileen pointed to a mass of it as they pressed deeper into the park.

"So you haven't forgotten!"

"No. Do you know, I seem to remember most things you taught me."

They unpacked a small cardboard box and ate their tea under a huge eucalyptus tree, and Eileen felt that never had she enjoyed a day so much. Daniel had a way of drawing her out as no one else had. She could voice to him thoughts that as a rule she kept deep down inside her. He never talked down to her or treated her as a child. He knew, in fact, that where her music was concerned, she was far in advance of her years both in her thoughts and accomplishments.

"Too big to carry now," he smiled, as they strolled

Daniel had a way of drawing her out . . .

(See page 154)

downward. The day was ending, and as they looked
down upon the city the shadow of Mount Eliza was
already thrown upon the Esplanade.

" It's been so lovely. Will I see you again ? "
Eileen asked eagerly, when at last he delivered her
back to school.

" Maybe, Eileen. I have a spot of travelling to do
before I go back to Tasmania. I'll turn up some time
and we'll fix up about Twink. And remember, keep
your eyes on the sun, for one day there will be a place
in it for you."

" I will, Daniel," and Eileen watched him walk
away with his long easy strides, wishing a little wistfully that she did not have to remain behind. But the
news Sister John had been waiting to tell her soon put
any such regrets out of her mind.

" Eileen, the great German pianist, Wilhelm Backhaus, is going to hear you play ! "

" What ? " Eileen could not believe she had
heard aright, and her knees seemed to turn to water.
She sat down very suddenly. She had read all about
this pianist, how he had won the Rubenstein Prize at
Paris in 1905. He was world-famous—and he was
going to hear her play !

" But how—why ? " she faltered.

" Because he is here in Perth and we have asked him
if he will."

" Suppose he doesn't like me ? What shall I do
then ? I don't expect I shall be able to play a note ! "

" Now, Eileen, stop working yourself up into a

state. You will be quite all right, only remember you must work hard until he comes."

"Oh, I will, really I will." And she hugged the surprised Sister John and danced the whole length of the cloisters from sheer good spirits, losing her few remaining marks from a lurking prefect for so doing. In the dormitory she got into further trouble for talking to Priscilla after "lights-out," and the next day she was kept in for inattention in class.

Soon, however, the school was humming with the news that Wilhelm Backhaus was going to hear Eileen play.

"It seems you are getting us talked about," Sadie teased.

"Really, girls, we shall feature in the papers soon," Nora joined in with mock reproof.

"Oh, Eileen, I'm so glad!" Priscilla said; "I was hoping you'd win a scholarship as I have to the School of Music, but this will lead you to far greater things, I am sure."

"If only it would; but I shall hate leaving all this." For the first time Eileen acknowledged the fact, and the next morning when she went to Mass with Priscilla she really felt a little weepy. Already her vivid imagination had carried her away across the sea, far from anyone she had ever known. Then for the next week she could hardly be persuaded to leave the piano.

"Where's Eileen? She should be playing games."

"Where is Eileen? She has missed prep."

" Where is Eileen ? She should have had her hair washed."

At last annoyed teachers gave up asking. They always got the same answer : " I expect she is practising." And gradually they also began to get the excitement running through the school. Wilhelm Backhaus was going to hear her play !

" And then what ? " Nora asked.

As usual, she had voiced what was in everyone's mind.

Then came the magic day. Eileen couldn't eat any breakfast and announced that she felt sick.

" But you can't be," Sadie expostulated with horror.

" Can't I ? " said Eileen, and promptly was. After that she felt considerably better, and had little sympathy for some of her band who discovered they also felt the same.

" But you haven't got to play ! " Eileen felt better with each display of nerves on someone else's part.

" Yes, but it's almost as if it was us ! " Priscilla explained, and all day she was around Eileen like a faithful watch-dog, seeing she did not get into any scrapes owing to the fact that she had relapsed into what she called " one of her trances ".

" He's come," Nora announced some time later. " He looks like one of those pictures you see of Liszt. I almost offered him my hair ribbon."

" Nora ! " Priscilla sounded really shocked that anyone should poke fun at the great master.

" Where is Eileen ? "

" They are dressing her up in a white dress just to make her more nervous ! " Sadie said miserably.

" It's funny, isn't it : here we all are, sitting on our thumbs for her, and when she first came we hadn't got a good word for her ! " Nora looked at the others as if surprised.

" Well, hang it all, the kid is a bit of a wonder where the piano is concerned."

Meanwhile, the cause of all the talk was grasping the future with her small firm hands and playing as never before. Maybe, even at that early age, Eileen had developed an instinct of what her audience wanted, a sympathetic contact with them that was always to stand her in good stead. The moment she came into the presence of Wilhelm Backhaus, all nervousness left her. She seemed to know what he expected and she gave it to him, and a great deal more in addition.

" I have heard nothing like it for twenty years. The child must go to Leipzig." Backhaus was on his feet the moment Eileen stopped playing, the fire of a discovery in his eyes. There was no beating about the bush : he made a statement to all those present and expected it to be acted upon.

" Leipzig ! " For a moment Eileen looked at him, startled. She had but a vague idea where it was. He sounded so definite that already everything seemed changed.

" Yes, Leipzig. There can be no other place for you."

" But there are many difficulties," Sister John ventured.

" They shall be overcome. They must be overcome.' Then, turning to Eileen, he spoke to her kindly and with great under- standing. She left his presence feeling that there was no longer any uncertainty about the future if she had the courage and will power to work for it. Her heart was beating fast, and yet she felt strangely calm, as if she had received a benediction. Quite unaware of heads peeping over banisters eager to hear the result, she flitted out of the building and made for the steps to the bathing pool, and there for a long time she sat and faced the future. Young as she was, she knew that she had a great gift such as was given to few, and that it was up to her what she made of it, should she by some miracle be sent away to develop it. She looked bravely at the dark side of the picture. She would have to go away quite alone. She would have to leave everyone she had ever cared for, even the only country he knew, and she would be desperately lonely. Then she remembered the acknowledgment she had seen in the eyes of Wilhelm Backhaus, and she knew that she would go on.

"Eileen, are you coming in?" It was Priscilla who had come to find her—a Priscilla who seemed a little awkward; who didn't know quite what to say.

"He liked my playing," Eileen said quite simply.

"Yes, yes, I know. Oh, Eileen, it was awful at first. When you ran out like that we thought it had been a flop; then Sister John told us, and now they are all planning what is to be done about it. They are going to try and get the fund really started to send you to Leipzig, and, of course, the school want a hand in it, too. Come on, come and see them all. Everyone is so excited."

"It's all rather like a dream. I don't feel like me at all," Eileen confided as they walked back.

"Well, I expect you'll soon lose a few marks, and then you'll know it's you," teased Priscilla. She noticed Eileen looked a bit white, and felt they had better get back to earth.

"Here is our genius!" Sadie shouted as she walked, a little shyly, into the common-room.

The other girls gathered round her asking questions. They were all obviously pleased and happy.

"I think you've earned some toffee!" Nora pressed some on her, and soon the look of strain had left Eileen's face and she was chewing happily, while

L

some of them pored over a geography book, trying to find out everything they could about Leipzig.

"I expect you'll come back an awful little German Frau with your hair scraped up in a bun!" Sadie warned her.

"No, I won't. Besides, I won't be away all that time." Quickly Eileen pushed any thought of years into the background.

"Well, it seems the problem is how to get you there, and we are all going to write no more letters to parents so that we can save our stamp money to help you!" Nora said amidst laughter.

"That will about pay for the hairpins of the famous star!" Sadie scraped her hair back and pulled a face at Eileen, who at once gave chase. Out of the room went Sadie with Eileen hard after her. Round the corner she fled, just avoiding one of the teachers carrying a tray of inkwells. Not so Eileen. Crash! she went into her, ink flying in all directions. The magic name of Wilhelm Backhaus cut no ice now. The wrath of the mistress who found herself sitting in the middle of the corridor, a pool of ink in her lap, knew no bounds. For the rest of the evening Eileen sat dolefully writing, "I must not run along corridors," until her hand ached and she wished that ink had never been invented.

A few weeks later the school learned that a fund, to be called the "Eileen Joyce Fund" had been opened in Perth as a result of Backhaus' visit. At the same time, the Mother Superior called the Sisters together, and with the usual kindness of their Order, they began to discuss ways and means. Two great musicians had made it plain that the child should be given her chance ; that she was, in fact, a genius, and so they decided that everything possible must be done to raise the necessary money. Eileen should go from the school with their blessing, and the fund should be supported in every way the school could think of. In addition, they decided to write to their members at Leipzig and find a suitable place for Eileen to live in.

" She seems so small to be sent to a foreign country all by herself. I do not think she realizes yet what it will mean," Sister John said thoughtfully.

" One of our Mothers will visit her from time to time as they pass through. You need have no fear, Sister John, that we shall lose contact with her," the Mother Superior promised.

" The matter of clothes ? " another asked.

" Yes, they must be provided. The child must be sent away with everything she will require."

" And when is Eileen to go ? "

" That depends upon the response to appeal for funds. As soon as we have the money she must lose no more time."

" Then it might be a year, or only a few months ? " Sister John asked.

" Yes, but it is too early to tell. Meanwhile, we can get to work."

The meeting was adjourned, and as soon as the result became known to the girls, the " Eileen Joyce

Fund " swept the school. One and all were eager to have some part in launching their school friend.

It happened that a business man of Perth, who had read Mr. Grainger's letter in the newspaper and become interested on hearing the views of Wilhelm Backhaus, came forward as a real benefactor. He gave Eileen his full support, organized concerts, and gave her the opportunity to play before the public. He even enabled her to earn money by her playing.

The townspeople of Perth were interested; they were quick to realize that they had a young genius in their midst. She belonged to Australia, and it would not be their fault if the world did not hear about her. Then, far away in Boulder City, Doreen heard of the excitement from the Joyces, and learned that they had given their consent. Straightway she wrote to the local paper, heading it for luck, "Wonder Child is to come into her own!" It started the ball rolling among the miners, who were only too ready to subscribe, and they at once set up their own fund.

CHAPTER XII

Off to Leipzig

'Look, Eileen! I've just copied this for you about Leipzig, from the encyclopædia.'' Priscilla took a piece of paper from her pocket and began to read. '' ' As a musical centre, Leipzig is known all over the world for its excellent Conservatorium, founded in 1843 by Mendelssohn. The series of concerts given annually in the Gewandhaus is also of world-wide reputation, and the operatic stage of Leipzig is deservedly ranked among the finest in Germany.' So, my love, it looks as if you are really going places ! ''

'' What's a Conservatorium ? '' asked Eileen, stumbling slightly over the word.

'' I looked it up in the dictionary. It means a public school of music. That's only the name they give it on the Continent.''

'' I shan't be able to understand a word anyone says ! What shall I do ? ''

'' Oh, I expect some of them will speak English, and if they don't you'll just have to learn German, that's all.''

'' That's all ! '' There was alarm in Eileen's voice. '' Oh dear, why couldn't it be America ! 'Cilla, I'm scared—scared stiff.''

'' You'll get over it. It's only the thought of

going that's worrying you. Why, when you really spend all day doing nothing but music, you'll be as happy as anything."

"I know I will. I wish you were coming, too."

"I wish I were; but come on—the minors have got a sweet stall in the hall on your behalf. You had better come and take an interest."

Eileen found the weeks that followed were full of such events. Every form in the school seemed to be doing something towards swelling the fund. Then began the concerts at which she played. Mrs. Morgan started by giving one in her drawing-room. Eileen enjoyed that; the house was very lovely, looking over the Swan River. Sadie and she were given a whole day's holiday in honour of the occasion, and wandered around the cool lawns or sat with soft drinks under a colourful umbrella, dabbling their feet in the water. After lunch it was time to get ready, and then Eileen got her first surprise.

"You are to dress in Sadie's room, and there is a frock on the bed for you," Mrs. Morgan told her, and Eileen could hardly believe her eyes when she beheld the lovely frock of pale pink chiffon which Mrs. Morgan had had made for her.

"That's right, child. Remember that colour suits you!" Mrs. Morgan nodded her approval when, flushed and happy, Eileen presented herself.

"Is it really for me?"

"Of course it is. You need a good frock if you are going to play in public."

Eileen thanked her gratefully, and as she sat and played light-heartedly to the first smart audience she had ever had, she began to feel that now at last she was contributing towards making her future career. The tickets were a high price, yet nobody thought them too high, for they were entranced by her playing. The kindly heart of Perth was stirred. Other people soon followed suit and threw their drawing-rooms open ; more and more people wanted to hear Eileen play. Cheques began arriving ; the child musician had caught the fancy of the public.

" Eileen, they want you in the sewing-room to try on a frock." Often the message would come, and away she would have to go, for the Sisters in the sewing-room were determined that she should not leave their care without a proper wardrobe.

" What is that ? " she asked with interest, as she noticed a green trunk standing open by the sewing-table.

" That's for you to take. One of the Art Students is going to paint your initials on it," Sister Mark told her.

" Oh ! " Eileen felt a cold chill run down her spine. It brought home to her the nearness of her departure—a thing she was now having to close her mind to.

" They tell me five hundred pounds has been collected already," Sister Mark continued.

" So much ? "

" Yes, but it is not enough."

" Then I shan't be going yet ? "

" Not quite yet. The last I heard they were trying to book you a passage in about a month's time."

" A month ! " Eileen left the room very thoughtfully.

Sister John found her unresponsive for the first time. " What is the matter, child ? Are you unhappy ? "

" No—no, I don't think so—it's just—— " But Eileen could not go on and turned her head away.

" I know, dear, you need not explain. The sooner you go now the easier it will be. It's just the waiting."

" Yes, that's it," Eileen said eagerly. " I want to go, but I hate it so much—the going I mean."

" Take my advice, Eileen ; you can afford to ease up with the practising for a while. Spend more time with your school friends."

" Yes, I think I will. I think I'll go for that picnic with them." She ran off to find the others.

" I am coming, too," she announced to Priscilla.

" Good. Miss James is taking us and we are going on a launch. Hurry up and get ready ! "

Eileen ran to join the scrum in the cloak-room, and soon they were all ready and started forth in high spirits. It was a care-free, happy afternoon. They put in at a little landing-stage, and carried their picnic hampers away into some woods where cool vine and white clematis carpeted the ground. They climbed trees, played hide-and-seek, and looked for nests, and Eileen loved the freedom of every moment. Tired but happy, they made the homeward journey clustered in the bows of the launch as it chugged peacefully along.

" Play your mouth-organ again," Sadie demanded, and Eileen, who usually took it on picnics, obligingly did so. They sang to her playing, and others rowing on the river waved to them as they passed, knowing they were the girls from Loreto, and enjoying their clear young voices and the happiness that went with the song.

" I shall miss all this," Eileen said, as she started home with Priscilla.

" Well, it's not over yet."

" But I expect I shall have to go home before I sail, and then the term will be finished."

The next day, however, brought Eileen fresh news. The Mother Superior sent for her.

" Eileen, the fund has nearly reached the sum of nine hundred pounds."

" Nine hundred pounds ! " Eileen looked at her incredulously. She had never heard of so much money.

" Yes, dear. It is a very wonderful response. It means that soon now you will be able to go. We are giving a farewell concert at the school for you at which you are to play. Arrangements are being made for you to live at a pension when you get to Leipzig."

" A pension ? " Eileen looked a little puzzled.

" Yes. It's a house where people go to stay. There is a very nice woman who will look after you."

" Oh ! " There was sudden unhappiness in Eileen's voice. " Please, may I go and see my parents ? I—I want to see them."

" We have arranged for your mother to come here."

" When ? "

" In a day or two, and you will have to go and meet her."

" Oh, thank you, thank you so much." The look of joy on Eileen's face more than repaid the Mother Superior for all the trouble she had taken.

" That is a very nice child," she remarked some time later to Sister John.

" Yes, Mother, I quite agree. She has character."

" I only hope success will not spoil her."

" I think that her very real love of music will pre-

vent that. I find humility in her where music is concerned; it is curious in one so young, yet it is there.
However well she plays, she always wants to play
better; she is her own hardest critic. It will be the
saving of her."

"I shall follow her career with great interest."

"As will we all. Eileen goes from here with the
good will of the whole school behind her."

"And our prayers will follow her. I think, Sister,
that we need have no fears for her success. She will
face the loneliness of the years ahead with courage."

Eileen was quite unaware of the doubts and fears
that assailed those who were launching her into a
foreign country, or the really warm hopes that went
with her. For the moment she was walking on air.
Her mother's arrival made everything safe and happy
for her again. Then came Daniel, having read in the
newspaper that she was soon to sail. It was a lovely,
exciting week that followed. Daniel took them all
to a theatre, and Priscilla was allowed to come as a
special concession. The two girls sat enraptured. It
was a variety show, and Eileen had never seen anything
like it before : the sound of the orchestra, the bright
lights, the brilliant colours and the changing scenes ;
but what thrilled them most of all were the jugglers.
They threw green and red dumb-bells, which sparkled
as they caught the light, and a party of men carelessly
juggled with plates which they spun on top of sticks,
passing them to each other as if it were the easiest
thing in the world to do.

"You had better not try that with the plates at school," Daniel warned.

Then as they strolled back to the school they talked about Twink. It was decided that Daniel should keep him while Eileen was away.

"Daniel, if I write Twink a letter, will you read it to him?"

"Of course I will," agreed Daniel, as if it were the most natural thing in the world.

"Eileen, you are silly. As if Twink would understand!" Priscilla could not help laughing.

"Of course he will understand. He knows everything I say;" and that evening Eileen wrote her letter.

Dear Twink,

I am going away but not for long. Please be good with Daniel, becos he loves you. Please Twink don't forget me. I will come back soon. Give my love to Tasmainia and old Jo. I wood like to take you with me but you wood be unhappy so I shall be unhappy without you. A kiss on your soft nose which Daniel will give you. Oh! Twink!

Love, Eileen.

Lessons still had to be done in the mornings, but every afternoon she was free to spend the time with her mother.

"Mummie, you do look nice. I've never seen you all dressed up before." She hugged her mother's arm as they walked to a little tea-shop which they had come to look upon as their own particular spot.

"Everyone has been so kind," Mrs. Joyce said. "Your father wanted to come, Eileen, but it just couldn't be managed.

"Oh, Mummie, won't it be fun! One day when I can really play I shall make some money, and we—we'll be able to spend it and have good times." Eileen looked at her mother with excited eyes as this thought suddenly struck her. "Will you be proud of me?"

"Very proud. But, Eileen, you won't forget to write, will you? You see, the years will pass, and if you don't write we shall get out of touch."

"The years!"

"Well, a few years. You see, you won't be able to run backwards and forwards between Germany and Austra-ia. That is why

we took rather a long time making up our minds."

"Oh—oh, I see. I had sort of hoped—but I suppose it's better to know."

"Hoped what?" her mother asked gently.

"That I would be able to come back from time to time."

"As things are I do not see how that can be managed."

"But you will get someone to write to me for you, won't you? Doreen would. I shall want letters. All about you and Dad and John and Uncle. It will be so far away. Oh, Mummie, I think I am silly to go!"

At the sudden despair in her daughter's voice, Mrs. Joyce realized that they were both very near throwing the whole thing up. She pulled herself together and smiled bravely at Eileen.

"No, child. We have gone so far, there is no going back. You are going to make me very proud of you and very happy, and you will be so busy the time will fly. Don't let's be sad any more."

"I won't go if you don't really want me to," Eileen said eagerly.

"I want you to go," her mother said very quietly, and after that they did not discuss it again, but each knew how the other was dreading the parting.

"Eileen, to-day is your big day!" Sadie announced two days later as they were getting up.

"As if she didn't know!" exclaimed Priscilla.

" Well, buck up; we've got to get the hall ready."

" Eileen hasn't got to."

" Oh, yes, she has. Much better for her to help us than mope around as she has been doing lately," Sadie said firmly.

" I haven't been moping! " Eileen sounded quite annoyed.

" Oh, yes, you have. Half the time you've looked like this—— " and Sadie pulled such a woebegone face that Eileen just had to laugh.

Breakfast, after chapel that morning, was a merry affair. It was a Saturday and there was to be no work, only preparation for Eileen's farewell concert. The gardener had already put great piles of flowers and foliage on the platform ready for the seniors to arrange. Minors were staggering along with chairs which seemed far bigger than themselves. Eileen found herself sweeping out the staff room and preparing the tables at which the guests were to have tea. There were cream cakes; iced cakes; little sandwiches with cress; fruit salad, and jellies.

" I'd like to slap my hand in the middle of that," Eileen announced as she put down a jelly.

" Eileen! Think of the headlines. I can see them now. ' Girl pianist slaps jelly in the face! ' No, no, my dear, it wouldn't do at all. Remember your public." Sadie, as usual, was mimicking someone.

" If Sadie doesn't go on the films I shall be surprised," Nora joined in. "Of course, it would have to be as a comic with a face like hers."

"What's the matter with my face? It's a very good face. Good enough to have custard pies thrown at, anyway."

"You've said it!" and Nora chuckled as Sadie seized a plateful of cakes and threatened to throw.

"Girls! Please!" Miss Burrows appeared at the door. "Eileen, you have to go and have your photograph taken for the Press. They are waiting in the front hall."

"Oh, golly!" Eileen looked around in alarm.

"I expect they want it as a record for the museum!" Sadie seized her hand and ran with her down the corridor. "Go on and look sad, dear child, look very sad. As you sail from our shores everyone will shake their heads over their papers and say, 'The poor wee mite!'"

This was too much for Eileen, and her eyes were still dancing with amusement as the reporter snapped her.

It was a day of mixed feelings for Eileen, a day of laughter not unmingled with tears. Everyone was so kind, so very kind and interested. Her school-fellows, as if aware of the strain she felt, rallied round and did their best to cheer her up. From the little waif she had at first seemed, she had almost become the mascot of the school.

At last the school hall was filled. The speeches were short and to the point. The Mother Superior, on

Eileen's behalf, thanked all those who had so generously put into her hands the chance of a happy and successful future.

Cheers broke out when it was announced that the fund had exceeded all expectations, the miners of Boulder City and Koolgardie having contributed largely. The head girl then announced that, as a token of appreciation for all that had been done for her, Eileen would, through her music, play her farewell and grateful thanks. It was the only way she knew of expressing how she really felt.

Amid fresh applause, Eileen walked to the piano. Her face was white, but she held her head high. Only her mother and Daniel guessed at the emotion she must be hiding.

" Poor kid, it must be an ordeal." Somebody in the audience voiced the thoughts of all.

Then Eileen began to play. She had chosen as her farewell piece Lieberstraume No. 3. It was her mother's favourite, and into it went all the hope, misery and uncertainty of adolescence—the fear of parting—mingled with the joy of having obtained her chance. It was all there for anyone who cared to understand. As her hands came to rest there was for a moment a silent pause of appreciation, then came the applause.

" Well, if the child can play like that now, we can expect big things of her," Daniel heard a critic remark quite excitedly.

Eileen certainly had surpassed all her other per-

M

formances ; and at last, with a nod from Sister John, she sat at the piano again. Very softly and simply, in a manner that lingered in their memories for long, she played to the delight of many, " To a Wild Rose," by McDowell. It was a peaceful finish, and showed an understanding of her audience that astounded many of them.

" Eileen, that was really lovely." Sister John bent down and kissed her pupil as she came off the stage. For a moment Eileen clung to her, then bolted to her form-room, where for a little while she hid, fighting back the tears that were now very near. Yet later the excitement of the moment seized her again. Happy and laughing, she joined in everything, carried round the cakes, answered questions politely and really enjoyed every moment. Sunday she was to spend with her mother, and later Daniel would join them. She hugged the thought jealously to her, and refused to think of the Monday, when she would sail away.

It was Sister John who, later that night, felt the urge to visit Eileen's bedside. There she found her swamped in the luxury of tears, with no one to witness the storm of doubts and fears that had assailed her in the darkness.

" Eileen, my dear child, this won't do." Sister John put a hand out to touch her shoulder gently.

" I don't want to go—please, I don't want to go. Please let me stay here and learn with you."

" But, my dear, I have taught you all I can."

Sister John pushed back the unruly mop of hair from the high forehead. " Listen, Eileen, you will soon make friends. Many friends. Remember how strange you felt when you first came here ? "

" But it's such a long way away. Right across the sea," sobbed Eileen.

" Distance makes no difference to those we love. Try to remember that our thoughts, our prayers and our hopes will all be with you. You will come back to us ; keep remembering that."

" But it will all be different—I know it will be different."

" Of course it will. You will be older and have accomplished what you set out to do. It will be in your power, Eileen, to give great pleasure wherever you go."

" Will it ? " The tears were abating now. There was a sudden flash of interest, and in a soft voice Sister John tried to tell her something of the life which she would lead as a student.

Sunday was over all too soon. It passed in a kind of haze, beginning with Mass with her mother and Daniel at her side. She was to spend the last night alone with her mother ; her luggage was to go straight to the ship.

" We shan't say good-bye ; we are coming down to the ship to-morrow," Sadie announced, when at last the moment to go had arrived.

" In case we don't get a word in edgeways, lots of luck and all that," Nora said awkwardly ; but

Priscilla couldn't say anything at all. Instead, she
slipped something into Eileen's hand and made a bolt
for it.

"Well, see you to-morrow." With a very twisted
smile Eileen walked from the recreation room for the
last time. Her good-byes were all said; there was
nothing now to do but to go. In the cab, she opened
her hand and found a thin gold bracelet—Priscilla's
greatest treasure. That night she slept clutching
her mother's hand, and as the time to go on board
drew near she became speechless with misery. Even
Daniel, who worked hard at it, failed to cheer her.
Then came the surprise. Just after her mother had
interviewed the stewardess in whose charge she was to
be, and as they returned to the gangway, her school-
fellows turned up in force. They boarded the ship
surrounding her, to the astonishment of the other
passengers.

"Look, Eileen, here are some sweets!"

"Eileen, this music case is with love from our
form! Think of us when you use it."

"Sister John says don't forget those octaves!"

And so the last few precious moments in Australia
passed, until the warning siren sounded and the cry of
"All ashore!" Everything was hurried then.
Eileen was conscious of warm hand-clasps, and
resolutely cheery good-byes; Daniel's "Now kid,
chin up, and show them what Australia can produce;"
the wrench as someone dragged her from her mother's
arms; a kind voice saying, "Come up on to the

bridge—you can wave to them from there;" the
curious who stared, wondering what all the fuss was
about; a loud voice declaring, "That's the kid
prodigy, Eileen Joyce. We'll hear of her again."

All seemed to come from a long way off as, looking
very small against the background of the ship,
Eileen waved farewell to the blurred mass she knew
must be below her. Then, without any fuss, the
great ship slipped her moorings. The journey had
begun, carrying Eileen away from the certainty of all
she knew to the uncertainty of a future that she alone
would have to make.

CHAPTER XIII

One of a Crowd

EILEEN had been in Leipzig some weeks before she found the courage to write her first letter home. The awful desire to cry when she thought of them all was not so acute as it had been, and she was beginning to find her way about. At the stationer's on the way to the Conservatoire of Music she had purchased some writing paper and a pencil. Now she sat in her tiny bedroom high up amongst the roof-stops, struggling with the first narrative of all that had happened to her since she had left.

Dear Mum and Dad,
  I hope you are quite well. I am having a nice time, are you? On the boat it was fun, people were very

kind to me. There was lots to eat and the Captain had me sit near his table, he had a beard. A nice man read me one of Daniel's books. I liked it, tell him. We went to England it was raining and had no sun, it is funny and small. I was met by a kind man in London who took me to his home, he was to do with the government. The next day he took me for a drive and I saw Buckingham Palace, it is where the King lives, and the Albert Hall where I shall play one day. Then I saw a fog and could not see any more, they have them in England. We caught a train and then a boat and then a train to Paris and saw the sun again. They all sound excited when they talk and I did not understand. Someone I smiled at wanted to paint me, but there was no time, and here I am in Leipzig. The place where I live is a tall house and there are lots of grown ups but no children, and I think Frau Hertz expected me to be bigger. I have been to the Conservatoire but no one has taken much notice of me. I am to study under Max Pauer, he is very important, I have seen him but he has not seen me. One of the Students is from America, says she will take me along when I have to go.

That is all I have to say. I would like to come home.

With love from Eileen.

The letter done, Eileen folded it carefully and addressed it, and decided she had better post it at once. She slipped cautiously out of her bedroom and peeped anxiously over the banisters. She did not want to meet Frau Hertz ; not that the Frau was unkind, but she had a way of looking at you as if you had no right to be there. Eileen had not quite got over the terrible feeling of desolation that had assailed her when the door had closed behind her escort, and she was quite alone for the first time in a strange land with no one to whom she felt she could turn. The unfamiliarity of the German house and German voices all round her emphasized the strangeness. She had expected to find someone else of her own age, but there was no one. It was a boarding-house, horribly quiet except for the opening and shutting of doors as their owners scurried to their rooms as if anxious not to be seen. The other boarders only emerged at meal-times and even then made no attempt at friendliness. Some had cast glances of displeasure at seeing a child of fourteen in their midst.

"Is this to become a nursery?" one old lady had remarked, glaring at her.

Frau Hertz had answered in German, and Eileen, not understanding, had been conscious of eyes directed at her in surprise. It was not to be wondered at, therefore, that in her loneliness she was anxious to hide away from people whom she did not understand. She got out of the house and into the main street without meeting anyone. She sniffed the air keenly; already there was a slight tang of coldness. She shivered slightly and hurried on. Instinctively her feet led her towards the old part of the town, which had already begun to fascinate her. She had seen nothing like it in Australia, and was thrilled by the narrow streets and old houses, with their high-pitched roofs, giving them a mediæval air which was enchanting to the child from a new continent. She would have explored farther, but was a little nervous of wandering too far afield for fear she got lost, as she felt no one would understand her if she asked the way.

Having posted her letter, she hesitated, wondering what to do with the hours until supper-time. She could not quite get used to the idea that it seemed to be nobody's business how she spent her time.

" Hullo, what are you up to ? "

Eileen jumped slightly at the sound of a friendly voice. Turning, she recognized the American girl.

" I—I don't know."

" Say, kid, are you all alone here ? " Norma Crawford looked at the slight, bewildered figure before her with faint surprise.

" Yes, I am." Eileen suddenly became embarrassed, and she felt the tears, always so near, ready to well into her eyes.

" I'll tell you

what we'll do. Let's go into the park and walk by
the river. Shall we ? "

" Oh, may we—could we ? " In a second Eileen
cheered up. For the first time someone had held out
a friendly hand.

" Yes, why not ? We are both strangers in a strange
land, and they don't talk our language, do they ? "
Norma turned and walked beside her, and Eileen,
shooting a quick glance, noticed how beautifully
dressed she was. Her figure was neat and she moved
as if the world belonged to her. To Eileen, Norma
seemed about twenty and quite grown up, but actually,
she was only seventeen.

" Well, tell me about yourself," Norma en-
couraged her, and as they pushed their way through
the crowded streets of jostling students, Eileen confided in her.

" Do you mean to say they sent you here quite
alone ? "

" Yes ; it—it was a long way."

" I should jolly well think it was ! Are you all
that good ? "

" I don't expect so," Eileen laughed, and Norma
liked her candour.

"Well, look here—don't you feel quite alone any
more. If you are in any bother, come and find me
and I'll also show you around a bit. I remember my
first year here ; it was devastating. But you'll love it
when you get to know the students ; there are quite
a number of fairly young ones. Now, what do you

think of the park ? '' Norma stopped to survey the
view before them.

'' It's lovely, but small after our country.''

'' Yes, I find the same, but at least there is some
space.''

'' What are those woods ? ''

'' The Rosenthal. We walk there sometimes on
Sundays. Would you like to come when we go ? ''

'' Yes, awfully.''

'' Very well, we'll fix it ; and now we had better
be getting back. The classes start to-morrow, so I'll
look out for you at the Conservatoire.''

'' What are you studying ? '' Eileen asked suddenly.

'' Singing, so our paths won't cross much at
work, but I'll show you a little café where you can
always find me. Until to-morrow, then '' ; and
having set Eileen on her way home, Norma left her.

That evening for the first time she did not feel quite
so forlorn, and she set out with a lighter heart the
next day for the Conservatoire. She passed the
new university library which looked vast and imposing. In mistake she almost turned into the School
of Art, but realized her error and found her way into
the Conservatoire. Inside, she stood bewildered.
There were so many students hurrying to their classes ;
nobody had time for one small girl who looked as if
she had strayed in there by mistake. Nervously she
asked someone where she should go.

'' Look on the board,'' was the only help she got.

After a great deal of difficulty she found it, and
scanning the notices, discovered her times and classes
" Harmony ; Counterpoint ; Orchestration ; Aural-
culture "—they all sounded strange to her ; but
strangest of all was her first lesson with Max Pauer.
She had expected an ordinary music lesson such as
she had had with Sister John, but instead, there were
others flocking into the room. Everyone seemed at
home, and she became more and more nervous as one
or two disinterested or surprised glances were directed
at her. There was a great deal of talk in various lan-
guages, until the great master himself entered. Then
you could hear a pin drop. A terse word and a student
got up to play, and as one followed another, Eileen
shrank more and more into the background. Their
playing was far in advance of anything she had ever
heard at school. A concerto was Greek to her ; yet
here one and all seemed brilliant in such work. Yet
the criticism some of them received from Max Pauer
left them in despair.

All too soon Eileen's turn came, and with a mind
completely blank she managed to reach the piano.
She was aware of Max Pauer's eyes upon her, ques-
tioning, wondering why so young a child should have
been sent to the Conservatoire. Somehow she pulled
herself together, and for the first time in her life when
she was playing her hands shook. Her confidence
seemed to have left her and her performance was very
ordinary ; yet it must have shown some promise had
she but realized it, for Max Pauer did not cast her

from his class at once. Instead, he made no comment, save to tell her to get certain music and work upon it and dismissed her without more ado.

It was a very chastened Eileen who came out with the others, especially when she heard one or two remarks :

" Fancy sending a kid like that to Pauer ! "

" She is miles behind everyone ! "

" Nothing like being in the kindergarten," a girl remarked, then a young man entered into the argument.

" I disagree. The child was nervous. She has something. Australian, isn't she ? "

They passed on, and Eileen felt a little cheered by the last speaker. Then her eyes brightened as she saw Norma walking towards her in the company of the man who had just spoken in her defence. They stopped when they saw her.

" David, this is Eileen, the kid I told you about."

" How do you do," David said gravely.

" Come and have some coffee with us."

" No, thank you, really."

" Yes, you will ; it will cheer you up." David refused to take no for an answer, so Eileen gave in.

" Why does Eileen want cheering up—what has happened ? " Norma asked with interest.

" I remember my first lesson with Pauer. I decided I'd chuck the whole thing up."

" Oh, did you ? " Eileen looked at him gratefully.

They turned into a cheerful café as she spoke.
There were students everywhere, sipping coffee,
talking merrily. Many of them greeted David and
Norma.

Eileen liked it at once. There were brightly
coloured check cloths on the tables, and the waiters
hurried amongst them in their white aprons. It was
the turn of the tide for Eileen, who found herself
sitting at a long table with many students of all ages.

" This is Eileen Joyce, and she is to be one of us,"
Norma said firmly, and although they did not take
much notice of her, she had found a corner at last.

" Where do you come from ? " asked a boy who
did not look very much older than herself.

" Australia."

" My name is Patrick. I come from Ireland. What's your name ? "

Eileen told him, and soon they were talking easily enough, and Eileen discovered that he was also a pianist.

" That means six hours a day for you," Patrick laughed.

" I don't mind that. I like playing, if only I could find somewhere to practice."

" Well, there's an empty practice room next to mine. You had better fix up for that. I'll take you along to-morrow."

And so it was that Eileen began at last to find her niche, and Norma, amused, saw that she would not have to worry about her quite so much, for young Patrick, who had no time for girls as a rule, soon found that Eileen and he had a lot in common. So much so that he firmly took charge of her, and Eileen soon found that instead of having to be continually anxious as to where and when she should go to various classes, she could leave it all to Patrick, who was usually near at hand to guide her.

" We'll go to the Gewandhaus this evening," he announced one day.

" What's that ? " Eileen enquired.

" The Gewandhaus ? Haven't you been there yet ? "

" No."

" It's where all the important concerts are held.

All the great musicians have played there in their time."

"Oh, do let's go." Eileen agreed excitedly.

"Got any money?"

"A little."

"Good. We shan't need much because we can get into the cheap seats. Meet me outside at seven-thirty."

From that day life took on quite a different aspect. Whenever there was a concert which she could attend, she was there. The atmosphere was like nothing she had ever imagined or felt in music before. The eager students hanging on every note; the audience, critical yet full of appreciation where it was merited; the musicians, world-famous, yet knowing that here nothing but their best would please; all this fired Eileen with a longing to reach their perfection. There were discussions after

the concerts amongst the students, and she listened eagerly, drinking in all that they had to say.

Then had come the awful day when a young pianist, who had already earned some fame abroad, returned and played in the Gewandhaus. He had appeared full of confidence and certain of the applause to which he was already becoming used. But as he played it was obvious that his style did not please the listeners, and Eileen, sensing it, suffered tortures on his behalf. As the applause failed to materialize, he looked exactly like a punctured balloon.

"It was awful, Patrick," she explained to him later as they sat with the other students. "I think if that were to happen to me I would not dare to play again."

"Oh, yes, you would," put in David. "Don't you know the story of Liszt when he came here?"

"No. What happened?" she asked eagerly.

"Well, he was quite famous by then, and came, certain of his reception; but as you've seen, the folk here don't just follow the fashion. They had their own opinion, and Liszt failed to please."

"How awful!" Eileen could hardly believe her ears.

"It was, rather. It upset the poor fellow so much that he took to his bed and postponed his next concert. When he did play again the same thing happened and it made him quite ill. Anyway, it gained him the friendship of Mendelssohn and Schumann whom he met here, so you see it doesn't always follow that if an audience fails to acclaim you at once you are a dud."

N

"I don't think anyone would agree that Liszt was a dud!" laughed Norma.

"Well, that's my point," said David. "It probably made him all the more determined to conquer the world."

"Anyway, it shows one thing. You really have got to be in a class above everyone else to really get a place in the musical world. I wonder how many of us stand a chance." Norma only summed up what many of them were thinking, but the blunt question shook Eileen more than she cared to show. Suddenly, and for the first time, she realized the high standard that would be required if she were to take her place among those who count. She was filled with despair. Only that morning she had displayed her ignorance to Pauer, who had earlier in the week told her to work upon a couple of Rachmaninoff's Preludes. Without the faintest idea of how to set about it when she did get hold of the pieces, she tried to master the music, but the result at her next lesson was many wrong notes. Pauer, half in earnest, yet more in humour, appealed to the class.

"Will you all subscribe to a cane which I can use upon Eileen to accentuate those wrong notes if they occur again?"

Poor Eileen, she took it all in deadly earnest, and this discussion did not help her. She flung herself into a frenzy of work, knowing that she had some years to catch up; but still her lessons with Pauer failed to give her the encouragement she needed, and she became more and more discouraged, certain that she would never reach the standard he required. Every spare moment that she had from classes she spent at the piano. Strung up to the highest pitch, she battled on and on, playing—playing—playing.

" I say, kid, whatever have you been up to ? " Norma, whom she had not seen for some weeks, stopped her in the corridor, She was quick to see Eileen's white face and rather strained expression.

" Working." Eileen smiled a little nervously.

" So I gathered. David tells me you have made the most amazing progress."

" Did he ? " There was eagerness in Eileen's voice.

" Yes ; he says he can't believe you are the same kid. He says even Pauer seems to be getting interested. But you can't go on at this pressure ; nobody can."

" But—but I've such a lot to catch up."

" You'll catch up all right. Now on Sunday we are going out to the woods and you are coming. Meet us at the café at twelve, and if you are not there I shall come and fetch you."

" I'll be there," Eileen agreed meekly, and went on her way.

" You know, David, Eileen is just working herself to a standstill," Norma remarked when she met him some time later.

" She certainly is a glutton for work," David laughed.

" Yes, but she is driving herself too hard. I must keep more of an eye on her."

" I don't see why you have to make yourself responsible for her."

" Well, I don't really, but she's a nice kid and there seems to be no one to look after her. It's just, I suppose, that she and I are both far away from home, and she is the youngest of us all and strikes me as a bit pathetic. Why, she is even growing out of her clothes."

" So I had noticed," David grinned.

" Well, I've told her to come with us on Sunday. She isn't getting enough fresh air."

" All right, Grandma," David teased. " I suppose that means the young Patrick as well."

" Probably," agreed Norma ; and sure enough he arrived with Eileen, and it proved the nicest day she had spent since her arrival in Leipzig.

The first snow had fallen ; the air was cutting and crisp, but the sun was shining. They walked through the lovely public park and into the woods of Rosenthal. Eileen loved the feel of the forest about her. She could shut her eyes and picture herself back in Tasmania. Patrick and she explored and climbed, and for a time became the children they were, stalking Norma and David as they strolled on ahead. They pelted them with snowballs, drawing them on to retaliation, and the woods rang with their laughter. David knew some people who lived on the fringe of the wood, so they called on them and received a warm

welcome. Round a huge log fire they sat while food was pressed upon them. Later, Eileen and Patrick were allowed to explore where they liked. The house was old, built of grey stone, with many gables. The floors of the hall were bricked and uneven. There were long, dark passages and low heavy doors.

" I bet there's a ghost ! " said Patrick.

" Where ? " asked Eileen, and looked nervously over her shoulder.

" Somewhere. All these old houses have ghosts ; at least they do in Ireland."

" I don't believe in ghosts," said Eileen, deciding it was the best attitude to take, for she saw Patrick was going to enlarge upon them in order to frighten her.

" Come on, let's go down here." They followed some old stone stairs and came to a tiny stone-walled room. There were iron rings in the walls and chains with handcuffs hanging from them.

" It's a dungeon ! " Patrick exclaimed excitedly. " They used to chain people to those."

" How awful ! " Eileen shivered and beat a hasty retreat. The thought of anyone with his hands chained to the wall filled her with horror. Out in the garden her spirits rose again. There was a large lake which already had a thin sheet of ice over it.

" You shall come and skate here," their host said as he came up behind them. " It should hold by next Sunday. Can you skate ? "

" I can," answered Patrick, but Eileen had to admit that she could not.

" You'll soon learn. I'll teach you myself," promised Herr Graf, and he was as good as his word, for after that they made many Sunday expeditions to the house near the wood. Eileen soon learned to skate, and was promoted from the support of a chair to gliding along by herself. Before long she and Patrick were racing madly together.

" Oh, it's such fun," she admitted gratefully one day, as she returned home with Norma.

" At least it has brought the roses back to your cheeks," Norma said with approval. " And I'll tell you something else. We have been asked there for Christmas, you and I."

" Oh, how lovely! I—I did not think I would have anywhere to go."

" That's what they thought, so we are to spend the whole day with them."

" What about David and Patrick?"

" They're going home, the lucky things."

" I wish we could," Eileen sounded wistful.

" Since we can't, this will be the next best thing, and you will have to wear your best frock. They all dress up."

" Oh dear. I seem to have grown out of it."

" Won't it let down?"

" I—I don't know. I haven't looked."

" Better bring it to me, and perhaps the old girl I live with will do something about it. Only don't forget. We have only about a fortnight now."

"No, I won't," agreed Eileen, and instead of dreading Christmas she really began to look forward to it.

CHAPTER XIV

Almost Despair !

EILEEN really enjoyed her first Christmas in Leipzig. She got up early and went to Mass—a
rather lonely little figure ; but somehow she did not
mind, for she knew the day was going to be full. It
was cold, and the whole town seemed quiet in the
snow. Sleighs passed with the soft, muffled thud of
the horses' hooves. Even the atmosphere of the
pension became more friendly. Breakfast was quite
a cheerful affair ; the room was decorated with holly
and a small Christmas-tree stood in the window.
Frau Hertz had actually put a present by Eileen's
plate, and when she unwrapped it she found a warm
scarf, for which she thanked her landlady very gratefully. Even the old lady who had objected to her at
first unbent and gave her a pencil. Upstairs, Eileen
opened a parcel she had saved up from home. There
were some sweets from John, a string of beads from
her father, some brightly coloured knitted gloves from
her mother, and in another parcel from Tasmania
addressed in Daniel's handwriting was a lovely photograph of Twink, sitting happily on the step of his
shack.

"Oh, Twink!" Eileen kissed it warmly and
hugged it to her for a moment, feeling a little tearful.

But Daniel's enclosed letter soon made her cheerful again, for he wrote of Twink's antics with Craig, and of all the things she liked to hear about. He also gave her fresh heart, for he finished up by saying he guessed how she must miss everyone at times, and how hard the work must be, but he knew the pioneer spirit would carry her to success, and that one day he would be very proud of her indeed. It gave her a nice warm glow inside, and she ran down, all smiles, to meet Norma.

Herr Graf had sent the sleigh for them, and in high spirits they bundled in and were wrapped around in a lovely fur rug. They sped along the snow-covered roads, little bells jingling on the horses' collars, and Eileen's eyes were dancing with excitement at the speed at which they were going.

" I'd like to go on and on for ever," she confided to Norma.

" What ! And miss our Christmas dinner ? " teased Norma.

" It's a lovely feeling though, isn't it ? "

" Yes, I must say it is. I don't know why you don't get the same sort of sensation on wheels."

Just then they drove out of the forest into the drive of the House by the Wood, and soon there were greetings and exchanges of wishes. There was a festive appearance everywhere ; already people were skating on the lake, and the three children of the house who were back for the holidays came to meet Norma and Eileen, surrounded by their dogs, who barked and jumped up, knocking Eileen backwards into a drift of snow. This broke the ice at once, and they all laughed, since Eileen did not mind at all. Then a great gong sounded, and they flocked into the house.

Eileen looked at the scene with eyes wide with astonishment. The main hall was decorated with holly and little lights. Down the whole of one side were Christmas-trees sparkling and glowing with many coloured candles. On the other side were little tables labelled with each person's name and loaded with exciting-looking parcels. Norma and Eileen found that they had not been left out, and Eileen longed to pinch some of hers so that she could guess what was inside them, but she found that there was a ritual to be gone through first.

The servants filed in, then the workers from the farms, their wives following with their children, and soon they were all singing carols lustily. Then Herr Graf gave them each a present, and they all drank his health and that of their mistress, and filed out happily to a feast in the servants' hall. Then in their turn the family and guests turned to their tables and undid their parcels. There were shrieks of joy and excitement as each gift was unwrapped. Eileen found she had a beautiful book bound in leather on the life of Mendelssohn—her first real book on music—a pair of skates, and some much-needed hair-ribbon—not that she ever remembered to use it. So the day wore on, a day of laughter and feasting, and a table loaded with food such as she had never seen before.

In the afternoon they went toboganning, and Eileen sat behind Rudolph, the eldest son, and clung to his belt tightly as they sped down a steep run, gathering speed all the way. It was a most thrilling experience, and she willingly helped him to pull the sledge up again in order to enjoy it all over again.

"I thought girls were afraid of going fast," Rudolph said in some surprise, in his stilted, clipped English.

" I am not. I love to go fast."

" Then I'll take you on a big run one day," he promised.

So it happened that the vacation passed happily enough for Eileen. Norma and she were always welcome ; but soon the holidays were over, and there followed for Eileen a year of hard grind into which she threw all her energy, and all her will ; she set herself a target from which she would let nothing distract her. Besides her music there were certain lessons she had to take.

The Symphony concerts at the Gewandhaus revealed a new world to her, and not for untold wealth would she have missed one. Bit by bit she saw into the mystery of the Concerto. She heard them all for the first time and listened in awe and wonderment, eager to reach the stage when she herself could master her technique and play them. With new zeal she threw herself into orchestration and counterpoint. She was determined to understand the why and wherefore of all she heard. As the months passed she began to find it easier to follow the score of the music at each con-

cert she attended. From being all at sea and behind
the others, she began to understand. Music ceased to
be just a rapture of sound that could raise her to the
heights and fling her to the depths. Instead, it became something she could interpret. Her aversion to
making a mistake kept her for hours at the piano ;
her desire to conquer and to understand made her
work on paper by the light of a candle hours after the
rest of her pension slept.

Norma, who was in her last year and expected to go
to Italy shortly, tried in vain to make Eileen ease up.

" The child seems obsessed," she remarked to
David.

" Drunk with music I should describe it," he
corrected ; " but she certainly is striding ahead and
beginning to attract attention."

" Yet she seems worried ! "

" I don't think she is quite happy in her lessons.
I, for one, feel she needs more individual attention.
After all, she was just plunged headlong into these
advanced classes, and it's given her a sort of anxiety
complex. Anyway, it's no good trying to stop her ;
she means to get somewhere, and we all know that
means hard slogging. Personally I prefer to take
things more easily, but then I've no particular desire
to be outstanding."

" You could be if you worked."

" Well, I do. And what about yourself ? You are
almost as bad as Eileen with your singing."

" I suppose I realize the competition," laughed

Norma; and soon after this she managed to drag
Eileen out to the House in the Wood, but somehow it
was not the same. Rudolph was home on a short
vacation, but he, too, was different. He seemed to
have a passion for dressing up in some kind of uni-
form. He criticized his parents and talked strangely,
and there was an air of unhappiness about the once
happy home. Norma was very quiet as they walked
back.

"I can't think what has come over Rudolph," was
her only comment to Eileen, and they did not go
there again. Soon their attention was focused upon
the Opera season, and they would sit together listening to the finest voices in Europe; and when Norma
said despairingly, "How can I ever hope to sing like
that?" Eileen would make encouraging replies.

All too soon the months slipped past, and Norma
had only a few days left. She had done well and was
leaving for Italy with high hope for her future.

"It will be hateful without you," Eileen said
sadly, the day before Norma's farewell party. "I
wish I were ready to leave as well."

"Well, you have some way to go yet, kid, but
you'll get there all right."

"Will I? You know, Norma, I don't feel I am
making the progress I should. I don't know what to
do about it. I don't feel Pauer is pleased with
me."

"Look, Eileen. It's no use getting yourself in a
state. You have only been here a year, and you are

working among some of the finest musicians. It's not to be wondered at that you are discouraged, but by next year I expect you will feel quite differently."

" Do you think so ? "

" I am quite certain of it, and don't you forget to write and tell me."

" I won't," promised Eileen, " but I shall miss you."

The following evening there was no time for regrets. Norma had collected all her fellow students together at the café and they sang and danced as only students can. Then they prevailed upon Norma to give them a farewell song, and they all gathered round the piano while she sang " One Fine Day " from Madame Butterfly. All too soon the party broke up, and early next morning she was off. Eileen was amongst the small party of friends who waved to her as the train drew out. Miserably she watched the distance increase between her and the one friend who had made her first year bearable.

" Good-bye ! " she shouted desperately as she ran after the train.

" Good-bye, kid, we'll meet again one day," Norma shouted back ; and with that cold comfort, Eileen faced yet another year with no one particular to whom she could turn, but Patrick, who had not returned last session, turned up the next, and soon they formed the habit of walking for miles every Sunday, sometimes alone and sometimes with others. It was Eileen's one recreation and she enjoyed it. Then her foot began to trouble her—why, she had no idea, and Patrick tried to re-assure her.

"I expect it's rheumatism; my mother has it."

She tried to be comforted, but soon the pain became more than she could bear and interfered with her pedal work. Then one day in the middle of a lesson she broke down, the pain was so acute. Everything went black, and when she came round she was in the hospital with a grave-looking doctor by her side. Very kindly he broke it to her that he would have to operate on her foot.

"But—but I can't be ill." She raised herself up in sudden panic.

"My dear child, you must leave this to me. I will make all arrangements and get in touch with the authorities."

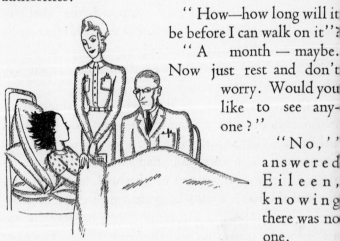

"How—how long will it be before I can walk on it"?

"A month — maybe. Now just rest and don't worry. Would you like to see anyone?"

"No," answered Eileen, knowing there was no one.

It was a trying time for her and a severe test of her courage. To be ill at home was bad enough, but to have an operation far away from everyone was agony to a sensitive mind. All went off successfully, however, and she was surrounded by kindness itself, for everyone in the hospital was sorry for the child who seemed so utterly alone. She cheered up a lot when Patrick was allowed to visit her and brought her some work to do.

" You are not missing much," he said; " fortunately you chose the right season to be laid up."

" But, Patrick, my practising and a whole term's work ! It's awful and—and the money, too."

" The money ? "

" Yes. You see, I've only a certain amount, and I'm so afraid it will run out before I've finished. I expect all this will cost a lot."

" Wait till it happens," said Patrick, boylike. " You will be out of here soon."

But when Eileen did get out, things were not too bright. She could only hobble about, and Frau Hertz, who had her hands full, was not very pleased at having Eileen to look after. Instead of being cared for and fussed over, Eileen found herself very much alone, and became more and more depressed. She became obsessed with the idea that her foot would always be stiff; that it would be no use on the pedal. She tortured herself with all sorts of doubts and fears, which failed to leave her until at last the moment came when she returned to the Conservatoire. Actually

o

she was strung up and nervous from the mental anxiety, and looked almost a ghost of her former self. However, she set-to once more with a will, and soon found that most of her imaginings were groundless. Her foot had quite recovered, and save for the loss of work there seemed little harm done—that is, until the authority in charge of her money sent for her. Then the blow really did fall. Her money really was running out. The pension had taken a large portion; her fees at the Conservatoire were eating up the rest. There was enough for one more session; after that—

" Well, she had better write home for more, or——"

" Write home for more ! " Eileen left the office in despair. Everything seemed suddenly to have turned against her. As Norma had prophesied, she really was, at last, feeling the result of her second year's hard work. She knew herself that she was making headway. To give it all up, just when things were becoming possible, would be a catastrophe.

" But why don't you write and tell them at home ?" asked Patrick.

" How can I ? My people have little money, and Loreto did so much for me. I can't write and ask for more." Eileen looked obstinate.

" Then I don't know what to suggest."

" P'raps I could get a job as a waitress in my spare time."

" But you never have any ! Besides, that wouldn't be enough."

" No, I suppose you are right. Oh, how I wish Norma were here to advise me."

" Well, she isn't," said Patrick, not very helpfully.

The session that followed was a painful one for Eileen. She scraped and saved every penny of pocket money she had. Her clothes were a sorry sight, but she would not buy new ones. She refused all invitations to the café and missed the extra food upon which she had come to depend, for the meals at the pension were not too hearty for a growing girl. She became pale and her nerves were strung up, and as a result she crossed swords with Pauer—a fatal thing to do, for his anger was great. Out of sympathy with her teacher, Eileen became more and more miserable ; yet not for an instant would she give ground. The advantage she had gained she meant to hang on to. She extracted every scrap of information and learning she could out of what she imagined to be her last term. She would practise to the last minute, rushing to the Concert-Hall just as she was in time to hear some special work.

It so happened that towards the end of the session, when already she had faced the fact that there was nothing else but to return to Australia, she left herself too little time and arrived at the hall to find the doors closed for the first movement. It was Tchaikovsky's No. 1 Concerto, which she especially wanted to hear. Unaware of two other late-comers, she sank down on the steps and rested her head on her knees. She felt

terribly tired and presented a sorry spectacle. Her hair was untidy; her dress was torn; she looked forlorn and uncared for and a pair of motherly eyes regarded her for a moment in some surprise. Then perhaps something in the dejection of the small figure prompted the owner of the motherly eyes to action. With a smile she went forward and spoke.

" How long do you think we will have to wait ? "

A pair of rather startled blue eyes looked up at her, and then a flashing smile. " Not very long. They open the doors after the first movement."

" Are you an Australian ? " The question surprised Eileen.

" Yes—why ? "

" We lived in New Zealand for years and so were neighbours ! Funny we should meet like this."

" Did you ? " Eileen got up with a feeling of excitement.

" Yes, my name is Mrs. Andreae and this is my husband."

" How do you do," Eileen said gravely. " My name is Eileen Joyce."

" Well, now we know each other. Are you staying here ? " Bit by bit Mrs. Andreae extracted from

Eileen a little of her history; then as the doors opened she suggested that Eileen should sit with them.

"But I've a seat with the students," Eileen explained.

"Never mind, come with us."

Eileen never forgot that evening. She felt happy and comfortable with someone from across the sea; yet her heart was so full at the thought of giving up her career that the music caught her unawares, and before she knew it tears silently streaked down her cheeks. They were not lost on Mrs. Andreae, who pretended not to notice but was all the more determined to find out all she could about the child. That she was unhappy was obvious, but the cause still remained to be discovered.

"Eileen, will you come and have tea with us in our flat to-morrow?" she asked kindly when the concert was over.

"Yes, please, I would like to."

"How long have you got here?" she asked.

"Er—I have to go back to Australia next month."

"But why?"

"Well, you see, my money has run out."

"Oh, I see. Well, we shall expect you to-morrow at four. Here is the address," and Mrs. Andreae handed her a card.

"There's something about that child that intrigues me," she confided to her husband as they walked home.

The next day Eileen arrived, having mended her dress and struggled with her hair. Mrs. Andreae made her sit beside her, and before long Eileen found herself telling her new friend quite simply all that had happened since she came to Leipzig.

"So you see," she finished, "all I can do is go back."

"No, I don't see," said Mrs. Andreae. "Something has got to be done about it."

CHAPTER XV

Headway at Last

IT was summer, and as Eileen stood on the Leipzig
platform waiting for the train to arrive there was an
air of excitement about her. Several people glanced at
her with interest, for she certainly looked attractive
and vivacious in a new well-cut green linen frock and
with her hair swept back from her forehead, its copper
tints catching the rays of the sun. Eileen was sixteen
and looked very different from the forlorn object
Mrs. Andreae had first set eyes on two years before.
There was an air of assurance about her now, and as
she waited for Norma, who was coming from Italy
for a refresher, somehow, Eileen turned to thinking of
all that had happened to her since they had last met.
From the moment she had met the Andreaes it seemed

as if a fairy wand had been waved, and the way made simple at last.

Mrs. Andreae's statement that '' something had to be done '' had proved no empty promise. In fact, she had set upon doing it then and there. She had combed Eileen's tangled mop, shown her some style of hair-dressing, and the next day had marched her off and bought her some clothes.

'' Now,'' she had said, '' you'll feel better. It's wonderful what a difference a few new things make, and you are never again to go about looking as if nobody cared about you.''

'' Well, nobody here did,'' Eileen had answered, truthfully enough.

'' Well, I do, and in future do not forget it,'' Mrs. Andreae admonished. After that she asked Eileen to play for them and Eileen arranged a short recital. The idea that had been fermenting in Mrs. Andreae's mind now began to take effect.

'' Eileen, you are going on with your studies here, and we are going to make ourselves responsible that you do.''

At first Eileen could not grasp that she had heard the magic words aright, and when they did sink in she was just speechless with happiness.

'' But why—why should you do this for me ? '' she asked in bewilderment.

'' Because, my child, you have obvious talent. You would never have been sent here had they not thought so in Australia. We both come from a long way away, and since we are here on the spot, well, we just feel we would like to help. After all, the Dominions must stand together, mustn't they?"

"It's wonderful—like a fairy tale;" and Eileen decided then and there that miracles did happen.

Mr. and Mrs. Andreae went into matters for her at the Conservatoire and there were one or two changes. For a long time Eileen had been thrilled with the teaching of Teichmüller, one of whose classes she had attended with a fellow student. She had longed desperately to become one of the great teacher's pupils, and now with the Andreaes' help the ambition was accomplished, a change that gave her nothing but happiness and assurance. She went ahead in the most amazing manner, finding the sympathy and understanding that she had missed. Mrs. Andreae also found her a happier place to live in, and she left the pension with little regret. She found herself, instead, with a kindly German family, and the mother of the house seemed to enjoy looking after her and watched her clothes with an eagle eye. It was no wonder, therefore, that she stood waiting for Norma a very different being from the rather ill-looking child Norma had last seen.

As the train drew in she caught sight of Norma, and waving frantically, was at the door by the time the train had stopped.

" Hullo, Eileen ! "

" Hullo, Norma ! How are you ? My, it's good to see you. I just couldn't believe it when I got your letter. You look marvellous ! " Eileen looked at her friend with admiration, for Norma really did look lovely.

" I must say I see a difference in you. What's happened to you ? "

" I'll tell you in the carriage. Here, porter ! " and Eileen grabbed one by the arm, and soon they were driving towards Eileen's room.

" You are going to stay with me. It's awfully nice and I couldn't bear you to go anywhere else."

" How did all this come about ? Your clothes— everything about you is different. You know, you are very naughty—you never wrote to me."

" I'm awful at letters, but I did send you a card."

" Lucky you did or I wouldn't have known you were here."

" And you—you have done well. I saw it in the papers."

" Yes, I've been very lucky ; but tell me about yourself."

" Well, I met some perfectly wonderful people called Andreae, and from that minute everything changed for me. It was like this " ; and eagerly Eileen told her friend of all that had happened.

" So you are with Teichmüller ! "

" Yes, and everything is just perfect. You can't imagine what a difference it made. He just swept me along. He wasn't just satisfied that I had a gift ; he ignored it and gave me the grounding I really needed. I am to play at a concert for charity next week. Will you come ? "

" Nothing will keep me away. Oh, Eileen, I am so very pleased for you. I have often wondered how things were turning out."

" Look, here we are ! " exclaimed Eileen, and soon they were unpacking and still talking hard. Norma, of course, wanted to visit all her old haunts and arrange for some lessons, and once again they went to the café and sat late over their coffee.

When they got back Eileen found a letter waiting for her from Mrs. Andreae. She tore it open and read it eagerly.

" They want me to go and live with them in England and make my début in London ! " she exclaimed excitedly.

" How lovely ! When ? " Norma asked.

" At the end of this term. You see, Herr Teichmüller thinks I am ready. Aren't they saints ? "

" They certainly seem good to you, but I think you deserve it, kid, for you are a jolly good worker."

" Thank you." Eileen shot her friend a quick, grateful glance.

" They sent me a cheque to buy a frock for the concert. Will you come and help me choose the stuff for it to-morrow ?   I think I'll have it made.''

"What fun !   Yes, I'll come with you.''

Before Eileen went to sleep that night she wrote to Daniel and told him all her news and that she was going to England.

> *And soon I shall be playing in public. I just cannot realize that the time has really come. Oh, Daniel, I do hope they will like me and that I make a success. There is so much I want to play. Patrick has left here and gone to America. He did very well. Write to me soon. I will send you my new address when I go there. I wonder how long before I have enough money to come to Australia, or perhaps I could play my way there, if not, you must come and hear me in England and we can cause a traffic block by gazing at the Tasmanian moon !*
>
> > *With love from,*
> > *Eileen.*
>
> *P.S. I've still got the mouth-organ you gave me and gave a recital in my room the other day.*
>
> *P.P.S. Mrs Andreae is going to have my photo taken when I get to England for " professional use ". Doesn't it sound grand ?   Perhaps I'll send you one.*
>
> > *E. J.*

The next day Eileen and Norma went to a dress-maker, and for the first time Eileen had a frock made for her by an expert. Norma helped to choose the stuff, and they selected a flowered voile, a white background with a pink pattern.

"Yes, that shade of pink is certainly your colour," the dressmaker voiced her approval.

"It's for a very special occasion: a first concert, and I want it to be picturesque," Eileen explained. "I am playing in a garden."

"Let us hope it will be fine for the Fraulëin, then." The dressmaker smiled at her as she took her measurements.

It proved a lovely day, and the public flocked towards the gardens of General Von Neudengraft's house. It was here the garden fête was to be held

under the fir trees which dominated the huge lawns. Stalls of all kinds and descriptions were arranged. Teas were laid down by the lake, and there were pony rides for the children and a miniature railway that was attracting a good deal of attention. A brass band played vigorously; the players looked hot and uncomfortable in their tight-fitting blue uniforms slashed with red. Eileen watched it all with fascination as she wandered round the gardens with Norma. There was a party of officers teasing a young girl who was selling flowers. Some small children, all in white, were dancing around a maypole, their hair scraped back, tightly plaited; and suddenly Eileen thought of Sadie and her forecast of how she would take to doing her hair in the German fashion. She laughed as she told Norma about it.

"Anything looking less German than you at this moment I could not imagine," was the reply; and then at last came the time for Eileen to be judged by the German public. The setting was perfect, for the piano was placed in front of a rock garden which was a blaze of colour and formed a half-circle round it. The audience sat on chairs on the lawn, and every chair was occupied. A tenor sang some folk songs; a violinist played most beautifully, accompanied by a chorus of birds that seemed attracted by the sound of his music. There was a murmur of approval as Eileen went to the piano, looking very young and dainty in her new frock.

"Looks like a picture with that setting," somebody whispered, and then she began to play. It was a happy choice—the Toccata and Fugue in D Minor, Bach—Reger—in keeping with the occasion. Oddly enough, she did not feel nervous. It was all so informal and friendly ; and playing out in the garden in such lovely surroundings, her thoughts turned to Daniel and her Tasmanian mountains, and the first time she had played her mouth-organ. She felt happy and lighthearted and full of confidence, and it showed in her playing. There was no doubt of the appreciation when she finished. The audience were quick to recognize her talent and were ready to show it. After her encore there were many who wished to be introduced to her, or made themselves known.

Meanwhile, Eric Von Neudengraft, son of the house, made himself known to Eileen and carried her off to the ice-cream counter.

" To-night we will dance," he told her.

" I do not dance very much," Eileen laughed ; " I have not had much time to learn."

" Then I will make it my business to teach you while you are in Leipzig."

" I am leaving for England quite soon."

" That is a pity. You should have played to us before."

" It is the first time I have been allowed to play in public. Was it all right ? "

" It was perfect. You should have a great career before you ; but they do not appreciate music in England. Why do you go there ? "

"I don't agree with you." Eileen felt suddenly annoyed. She felt that the German was sneering at the Mother Country and was quick in defence.

"It is a matter of opinion," Eric answered stiffly; then in a lighter vein, "Come, let's dance; they are beginning."

Eileen enjoyed that evening. She was introduced to fellow officers of Eric's, and Norma was annexed at once. They were all very young, yet danced with an ease that Eileen could not imagine Patrick doing. She found their steps easy to follow, and having music in her, discovered that she was a natural dancer. Little fairy lights lit up the lawn as darkness fell, and Eileen, as she glided on Eric's arm, felt she had never enjoyed anything so much since that first Christmas at the House in the Wood.

"I am very lucky," she said suddenly, as they walked back to the refreshment tables.

"Why?" Eric asked.

"To-day has been so lovely, and to-morrow I hear Beethoven's Fourth Concerto at the Gewandhaus."

"Is that your favourite work?"

"Yes, it is my greatest treat to hear anything of his, but above all the Fourth. Do you know it?"

"Well, I expect I've heard it, but I am not music-minded like you, and know everything just as the Fourth or Second, if you know what I mean." For a moment Eric was embarrassed. He felt he was being weighed up and found wanting; then he brightened suddenly, and, seizing her hand, ran with her across the lawns. They dodged in and out of dancing, laughing couples.

" Where are we going ? " Eileen gasped.

" I've had an idea. You shall educate me ! "

And Eileen found that they were back in the rock garden and that the piano was still there.

" Naughty of someone to leave it out so late," she said, as Eric opened it.

" It won't hurt on a night like this. Now play to me—this Fourth, I mean."

" The first movement, anyway ; " and Eileen sat down and to her audience of one played passages from the work she most loved. In the woods a nightingale sang, and Norma, coming to find her, stood entranced, for she thought she had never heard anything so haunting as that piano music, in the stillness of the night. Eileen seemed so much a part of her surroundings as, with her eyes closed, she played oblivious to everything but the interpretation of the composer's work.

Eileen went to bed in a dream that night. She

P

wondered if Herr Teichmüller would have anything to
say about her first public performance, but he ex-
pressed nothing but pleasure at the short Press notice
she received. His young pupil was beginning to
prove the faith he had in her.

"When you go to England I will write you a letter
to take to Mr. Albert Coates. I know he will give
you assistance," he promised, and in a happy frame
of mind, Eileen settled to her lesson. Every moment
became more and more precious to her. To Eric's
entreaties that she should allow him to show her more
of the sights she turned a deaf ear. He was a good
companion and she liked him, but not for a moment
would she lose any precious time for work. Six
seven hours a day she practised; for only perfection
would she bring to Herr Teichmüller. He expected
it and he got it. She had done brilliantly, and knew
now that she would go from Leipzig with the power
to succeed in her hands; that the faith of those in
Australia had not been misplaced. The gratitude she
felt to her teacher she could not begin to express; she
could only show him by her will to work how much
she appreciated all he had done.

Eileen's last weeks were happy and crowded
Many students had finished their course; there seemed
to be farewell parties most evenings. Music, song
laughter and dancing; it was a gay, happy finish to
very hard work. Norma and she had made the most
of their time together. On the very ordinary piano
at the café Eileen would contribute to the enjoy

ment of the party, causing a silence in which you could hear a pin drop ; or listen enchanted to Norma's glorious voice.

" I shall miss all this," Eileen said to one of the students.

" Won't we all," he agreed. " Once we have left here our job will be to make music. We shall then not have so much time to appreciate the talent of others, the talent we have taken as a matter of course."

" I wonder what England will be like."

" The English are hard taskmasters to start with."

" But they are very fair, the English."

" It's not so much a question of that as of opportunity."

" Well, somehow I must make the opportunity."

So days flashed past and Eileen soaked herself in music every hour of the day. Nothing of importance was played that she did not manage somehow to hear. She heard Prokofiev's Concerto, at which she had been working, and was glad of the insight it gave her into the work. She listened again to Grieg's Concerto in A Minor. It had been the first Concerto she heard in Leipzig, and she was gripped again as she always was by the emotional climax of the first movement, and haunted by the melody of the third. The fact that when Grieg went to Leipzig for the first time he was only a year younger than she was now, kept flitting before her mind. He also was on the threshold of success, and as she closed her eyes, listening to the beauty of his work, she could almost imagine him as he must have been on that very stage, playing for the first time his own Concerto.

As she walked home under the starlit sky, with the great clanging chords still ringing in her head, she longed with all her heart for the opportunity to prove that she could interpret such music if given a chance ; but next day, at her last lesson with Herr Teich-müller, she felt suddenly apprehensive and was filled with a childish panic. With him behind her she had felt full of confidence ; but now had come the moment when she would have to stand alone and prove to an overwhelming world that she had the right to be heard.

It was a bad moment, that moment of parting ; but the great master seemed to understand her feeling, and his quiet assurance did much to calm her. She had been through much to reach this moment, the moment that brought her face to face with her career, and she left him with the knowledge that she had his confidence.

With her good-byes all said and plans made for meeting Norma later, there was nothing for it but to leave the city that had come to mean so much to her. But this time it was not so bad as when she had left Australia. True, she was going to England, another unknown country to her, but this time there was someone waiting for her, someone who would be at her back while she made her début into the world of professional musicians. She meant to make the name Eileen Joyce known to the world. No longer would she be one of a crowd.

CHAPTER XVI

A Proud Moment

ENGLAND! Eileen could hardly realize that this was the same country as the foggy place she had visited in such lonely circumstances three years ago. The sun was shining and the sky was blue. The people looked gayer and more picturesque dressed in their summer frocks.

The Andreaes had been waiting for her on the platform as the boat train steamed in. Eileen felt it was like a homecoming, the first she had experienced for many years. They had gone to an hotel, and the next day had shopped, and Eileen had been introduced to her first English theatre. The play was Henry the Fifth, Eileen's first experience of Shakespeare, and she was thrilled.

" I seem to see everything worth seeing for the first time with you," she remarked, as they were going up to bed.

" Yes, we saw Pavlova together, didn't we ? " Mr. Andreae answered, for he guessed to what she was referring. He had never forgotten Eileen's reaction to the great dancer when they had taken her to the ballet in Leipzig. The child had seemed hypnotized by the rhythm and beauty of movement which she was quick to appreciate.

"Well, let us hope it is the beginning of many nice new experiences for you. To-morrow we shall see what you think of the English country, for we are going down to our house."

It was a great moment for her when she saw the house which was going to mean home to her. They had it built while she was in Leipzig and her joy in it knew no bounds.

"And now we have a surprise for you." The Andreaes took her out into the garden, and there, away from the main building so that she could work without disturbance, was a music-room and in it a most beautiful Blüthner piano.

"I must be dreaming! How can I ever thank you?" In an ecstasy of happiness, she sat down and played.

They were grand months that followed. For the first time almost since leaving Tasmania Eileen felt free : free to come and go as she pleased ; free to play to her heart's content ; free to explore the countryside, to come home tired but happy ; to eat poached eggs—a special weakness of hers—at all hours of the day. Sometimes, after hours at the piano, she would curl up in a chair and go to sleep, in spite of anything that was going on around her.

"She is just like a kitten," Mr. Andreae had said with amusement.

"Working as she does, that capacity to fall asleep instantly will stand her in good stead in the future," his wife pointed out.

One morning the whole house was awakened by a terrified cry from Eileen's bedroom.

"Come—oh, please come quickly!" There was such terror in her voice that Mrs. Andreae rushed to Eileen, expecting to find some terrible tragedy being enacted. Instead, she found Eileen standing on the bed, looking with horror towards the window.

"Eileen, what is it?" Mrs. Andreae went to her quickly.

"Over there—that—that terrible creature!" Eileen pointed. She was quite white, and Mrs. Andreae advanced hastily towards the window, and then she saw the object of Eileen's dismay.

"It's a daddy-long-legs! Oh, you poor child!" Mrs. Andreae could not resist laughing, partly from relief. "It's a most harmless insect and most common. Look, I'll catch it;" but the daddy-long-legs had different ideas and flew out of reach.

"How silly of me." Eileen was laughing herself now. "I thought it was some poisonous insect like the ones we have at home."

"You won't find anything like that here. Come on, let's go and have breakfast."

The adventure over, the day passed peacefully enough until, as they were having tea, a cuckoo flew over.

"What is it? What a strange song it has. I like it."

"That's our English cuckoo, but I expect you will soon get tired of him," Mr. Andreae said.

" No, I won't. I've never heard anything like it before ! "

But Mr. Andreae was right : only two days later he heard Eileen shouting at it in a fury to be quiet.

" What did I say ? " he laughed.

" It's that incessant third," stormed Eileen. " It drives me mad. If only he could change it a little ! "

" Well, he won't, so you had better get used to it, like many things over here. It's the only piece he has learnt ; " at which they both laughed.

Soon after that they began to discuss plans for a recital they wanted Eileen to give.

" I feel it would be a good idea. It will bring you to the attention of people before you go to London. It may lead to helpful introductions," Mrs. Andreae advised.

" The question is, where ? " Mrs. Andreae interposed.

After a good deal of discussion they decided upon Norwich.

" It's a big town and the people are musical," Mrs. Andreae explained.

" I wonder what kind of programme they would like," Eileen said thoughtfully, and for days she pored over her music, trying to decide. It was a thrilling time, and she loved every moment of it. At last, after a great deal of consideration, she finally selected her programme, and then for days the Andreaes hardly saw anything of her, for she retreated to her music-room and worked the days away.

" You have got to spare time for the dressmaker," Mrs. Andreae pointed out at last, in despair.

" I had forgotten all about it," Eileen admitted rather shamefacedly, but soon she was quite ready to give up time for fittings.

The dress was the loveliest she had ever seen, the colour of maize. It fell in soft flounces to her feet, and round her waist was a heavy sash of a deeper shade. There was a little gasp of pleasure when, on the day, she came on to the flower-decked stage which Mrs. Andreae had spent hours decorating. Her youthfulness and charm of manner won the hearts of her audience, and they sat back, ready to be enchanted by this young player, hoping, maybe, that her playing would be as delightful as the picture she made. Soon there was a little stir of excitement, hardly perceptible at first ; but as the strength and personality of the player began to make itself felt, the audience realized that here was no ordinary girl pianist, but one of extraordinary talent.

The Andreaes had been right. The musical people of Norwich, by the end of the recital, were only too ready to make the acquaintance of their new discovery. Eileen found herself talking happily to real music-lovers, some of whom had influence in the music world. Introductions were showered upon her, everyone seemed only too anxious to help her.

" I find everyone so kind over here," she remarked happily as, hours later, she strolled in the garden with the Andreaes. " I think it was a success."

" My dear, the applause should have told you that if nothing else."

" I am so glad. I was terribly nervous."

" Well, you did not show it. A more composed young woman I never saw."

" I have to thank Teichmüller for that. He seems to have given me all the confidence in the world."

" And that is half the battle," Mrs. Andreae told her.

All too soon those happy, care-free days came to an end, for they all realized that the moment had come for Eileen to go to London.

" We will find you a studio where you can work. You must make use of your introductions and take your letter to Albert Coates. This is the beginning, Eilie. Do you feel ready for it ? " Mrs. Andreae slipped her arm through Eileen's as they were walking back from the music-room.

It was dusk, and in the small spinney not far away a nightingale was singing. For a moment Eileen stood still and listened, then she said softly, " I have never felt readier for anything in my life, thanks chiefly to you."

" And Herr Teichmüller ! "

" And Herr Teichmüller," Eileen echoed.

The next day they went to London and the search for a studio began. They found one at last, in a perfect spot with an old fig tree peeping in at the window.

" I shall pretend it is your garden," Eileen said a little shakily.

So at last it came about that Eileen was ready to use one of her introductions. The day came when she went to Albert Coates, a day for which she had been preparing. Once he had heard her play, as Herr Teichmüller had predicted, he was only too ready and willing to help.

"I shall bring you to the attention of Sir Henry Wood," he promised.

It was more than Eileen had dared hope, and once again she went through those days at Loreto when she had waited and waited to hear from Percy Grainger; but this time she hadn't to wait so long. She had only just begun to convince herself that the great conductor would not want to hear her when the summons came.

It was a great moment for Eileen—her first meeting with Sir Henry Wood. Any fears she may have had vanished before the warm, big-hearted generosity of this fine, dynamic leader of British music. She realized at once that only if she could prove herself worthy of the perfection in music which he required would she be given his support. He was obviously interested in this young pianist from across the sea, but she was quick to feel the challenge he made her. It put her on her mettle, and made her determined to answer with every bit of music that was in her, so she sat down and played as he asked, and found only joy in playing to a great musician whom she knew would hear her with fairness. That she had won his approval was apparent at once. No true musician ever passed unnoticed by Sir Henry, and he found in Eileen that quality for which he looked. Young as she was, he recognized her talent.

The Queen's Hall—a coveted Promenade Concert— and above all, the little known Prokofiev Concerto. At first she could hardly grasp the full meaning of it all. Sir Henry's words and arrangements for her, his appreciation, seemed to elude her mind. She could not realize that this was happening to her.

" Now then, Miss "—a policeman seized her arm as she was about to step into the roadway, oblivious of the traffic. It brought her down to earth with a crash, and she looked at the man in blue with some bewilderment.

" What's the matter ? Had a shock ? " he asked kindly.

" Yes, I've had a shock, but it's a very nice one." Then quite suddenly everything became very real, and with a smile at the fatherly policeman, she hurried away to a telephone kiosk.

The Andreaes were her first thought. In an excited voice she told them the news.

" I am coming down on the next train—I just can't stay in London another minute. I feel I want to run and run ! "

" Well, there's plenty of space to run down here," Mrs. Andreae answered happily, and it was a very few hours later that an extremely happy Eileen was with them, telling them every detail of the eventful interview. She walked that evening and found the highest hill she could, but in her mind she was running wildly up the mountain path in Tasmania to a little shack half-way up. She wanted very much to tell Daniel that the moment he had foreseen for her had come at last.

There was little time left to Eileen for dreaming after her few peaceful days. Rehearsals were to start shortly, and before that she must put in days of practising. Nothing could interfere with that. Back in her studio she soon settled down again, for six hours a day. She was lost to everyone, but was utterly and completely happy. Some evenings she would go to the Proms, and there in the unforgettable atmosphere of the Queen's Hall she watched Sir Henry Wood from her lofty seat in the "gods" until she began to gain some understanding of his handling of an orchestra.

The days passed swiftly enough; then came the time for rehearsals. Eileen found them exciting and enlightening. She was on the top of her form all the time; Sir Henry seemed to have that effect upon her.

"I feel rather like a bottle of champagne when I am working with him," she confided to Mrs. Andreae.

In between the rehearsals she had to submit to a hairdresser and yet another dressmaker, but this time she took it as all part of her profession. She knew how much it helped to feel well dressed. The great day arrived at last, a day for Eileen of wild happiness and sudden despair. One minute she was certain of herself, the next full of doubts. She felt bubbly, nervous, demented, thrilled, miserable, hopeful, all within the course of a few minutes. She could hardly bear to speak to anyone, yet she wanted to be with people. Then, as the time drew near, and she arrived at the Queen's Hall, Sir Henry Wood's hand-clasp, his kind words of assurance, brought to her a return of confidence, and as the great hall was filling she was able to sit quietly in her dressing-room, her thoughts only of the music.

When later she walked on to the platform there was not a sign of the emotions which had surged through her, and the Andreaes, watching her, relaxed in their seats, for they knew her well enough to recognize that she had regained her confidence.

The work chosen was a happy one. The Prokofiev Concerto is of the modern school. It is full of happiness and gaiety, and as Eileen played she entered into the spirit of the work and the magic of Sir Henry's conducting.

When, towards the end, the note of romanticism stole in, it was still in keeping with her mood; for, after all, from the time when she was a little ragged girl in Tasmania to that moment at the Queen's Hall her life had been a romance in itself.

As the applause broke out and she knew she had not failed all those who had faith in her, her happiness was complete. Her professional career had begun. She had played to the great British public and their applause proved that they liked her. As she turned from the stage and vanished into the artistes' room

" *Her professional career had begun.* "

(*See page* 238)

there was a gladness about her and a new bearing in her manner. She knew that there was a long struggle ahead, but she was standing on her own feet at last. Sir Henry Wood had given her the opportunity to be heard ; it was up to her to go forward from there. She faced the future with clear, fearless eyes, determined to make good.